¡Qué chévere!

Level 1

Workbook

Karin D. Fajardo

ST. PAUL, MINNESOTA

Associate Publisher
Alex Vargas

Development Editor
Kristin Hoffman

Senior Designer
Leslie Anderson

Production Editor
Bob Dreas

Cartoon Illustrator
Kristen M. Copham Kuelbs

Senior Digital Production Specialist
Julie Johnston

Digital Production Specialist
Sara Schmidt-Boldon

ISBN 978-0-82196-924-3 (print)

875 Montreal Way
St. Paul, MN 55102
E-mail: educate@emcp.com
Web site: www.emcp.com

Printed in the United States of America

24 23 22 21 20 19 18 17 16 5 6 7 8 9 10

Nombre: ______________________________ Fecha: ______________

Unidad 1

Lección A

1 ¡Hola!

Unscramble the following conversation between two new students. Number each line 1–7 to show the correct order.

_______ ¡Hola! ¿Cómo te llamas?

_______ ¡Adiós, Natalia!

_______ Yo me llamo Luis.

_______ Se escribe con ele mayúscula, u, i, ese.

_______ Hasta luego, Luis.

_______ ¡Mucho gusto! ¿Cómo se escribe Luis?

_______ Me llamo Natalia. ¿Y tú?

2 ¿Cómo se escribe?

Look at the following listing of the editorial staff of a Spanish-language magazine. Find the first name that corresponds to each clue and write it in the space provided.

FURIA MUSICAL

DIRECTORA EDITORIAL
Blanca Martínez

COORDINADOR EDITORIAL
Eleazar Ramos

DIRECTOR DE ARTE Y DISEÑO
L. Daniel Martínez V.

ARTE Y DISEÑO:
Jacqueline Buenrostro y Mitzi Solano

REPORTEROS:
Oscar Vargas C. y Antonio Arciniega

COLABORADORES:
Polo López, Héctor Pérez, Israel Sedano.

CORRECCIÓN DE ESTILO:
Ana María Cortés C.

FOTÓGRAFOS:
Miguel Mendívil, Miguel Marín, Blanca Charolet y Jaime Nogales.

CORRESPONSALES EN CALIFORNIA:
Yanalte Galván, José A. Hernández y Félix Castillo.

CORRESPONSAL MONTERREY:
Sara Sánchez

DIRECTOR GENERAL DE VENTAS DE PUBLICIDAD INTERNACIONAL:
Roberto Sroka

GERENTE DE VENTAS DE PUBLICIDAD INTERNACIONAL:
José R. Vila

Tel: (305) 871 6400 Ext. 214
Conmutador: (525) 261 2670
Redacción: (525) 261 2634 y 261 2635.
Fax 261 2730.
E-mail: furia.musical@editorial.televisa.com.mx

FURIA MUSICAL ES UNA PUBLICACIÓN DE EDITORIAL TELEVISA

VICEPRESIDENTE DE OPERACIONES USA Y SUDAMÉRICA
Eduardo Michelsen

VICEPRESIDENTE EDITORIAL
Irene Carol

VICEPRESIDENTE DE OPERACIONES
Raúl Braulio Martínez

VICEPRESIDENTE DE ADMINISTRACIÓN Y FINANZAS
Sergio Carrera Dávila

1. Se escribe con ye mayúscula.

____

2. Se escribe con hache mayúscula.

____

3. Se escribe con eme mayúscula, i, te, zeta, i.

____

4. Se escribe con equis minúscula.

____

5. Se escribe con u con acento.

____

Nombre: ______________________________ Fecha: ______________

3 Sopa de letras

In the word square find and circle ten Spanish names. The words may read vertically, horizontally or diagonally.

Z	A	W	S	D	G	H	K	Q	Ú
O	P	I	L	A	R	É	P	O	I
X	C	F	V	F	B	N	M	Á	R
V	É	E	D	E	G	U	H	L	A
E	S	D	O	L	O	R	E	S	Q
J	A	E	R	I	T	Y	R	F	U
O	U	W	B	P	P	G	N	S	E
R	Z	A	T	E	A	I	Á	D	L
G	C	V	N	Y	B	A	N	F	G
E	Q	Ú	S	É	L	C	V	É	B
A	U	T	G	L	O	R	I	A	S
R	W	Á	I	X	M	I	N	K	L

Nombre: ______________________________ Fecha: ______________

4 Puntuación

Rewrite the following sentences with the correct punctuation.

1. Hola! Cómo te llamas?

____

2. Mucho gusto, Sonia!

____

3. ¿Cómo se escribe Javier? Con jota?

____

4. Yo me llamo Antonio. ¿Y tú.

____

5. Hasta luego, Beatriz!

____

6. ¡Adiós, Ricardo.

____

5 Celebraciones y saludos

Decide whether each of the following statements about Spanish-speaking culture is *cierto* (true) or *falso* (false). Write **C** or **F** in the space provided.

______ 1. Birthday parties may last until the early morning hours.

______ 2. A girl's fifteenth birthday is a very special occasion.

______ 3. Boys celebrate their fifteenth birthday with a formal dance in a banquet hall.

______ 4. Men exchange a handshake and a hug when greeting friends and relatives.

______ 5. Men and women who do not know each other may exchange a kiss on the cheek.

______ 6. There is no verbal exchange among Spanish-speaking people when they greet each other.

Nombre: ______________________________ Fecha: ______________

6 América del Norte, América Central y el Caribe

Identify the Spanish-speaking countries in the following map. Write the name of each country in the space provided. You may refer to the maps of Central America, Mexico and the Caribbean in the textbook.

Costa Rica	El Salvador	Honduras	Nicaragua	Puerto Rico
Cuba	Guatemala	México	Panamá	República Dominicana

1. ______________________________ 6. ______________________________

2. ______________________________ 7. ______________________________

3. ______________________________ 8. ______________________________

4. ______________________________ 9. ______________________________

5. ______________________________ 10. ______________________________

Nombre: ______________________________ Fecha: ______________

7 Europa, África y América del Sur

Write the names of the Spanish-speaking countries indicated by each number. Refer to the maps of Europe, Africa and South America in the textbook.

Nombre: ______________________________ Fecha: ______________

8 Matemáticas

Write a number word in Spanish to answer each math problem.

MODELO: 1 + 2 = tres

1. 2 + 3 = ______________________
2. 4 + 5 = ______________________
3. 9 – 2 = ______________________
4. 10 x 2 = ______________________
5. 6 + 6 = ______________________
6. 8 x 2 = ______________________
7. 19 – 9 = ______________________
8. 5 x 3 = ______________________
9. 12 – 4 = ______________________
10. 10 + 4 = ______________________

9 Más números

Following the pattern, write the next number word.

MODELO: cuatro, ocho, doce, dieciséis

1. dos, cuatro, seis, ocho, ______________________
2. cero, cinco, diez, quince, ______________________
3. uno, cinco, nueve, trece, ______________________
4. veinte, dieciocho, dieciséis, ______________________
5. quince, catorce, trece, doce, ______________________
6. tres, seis, nueve, doce, ______________________
7. doce, catorce, dieciséis, ______________________
8. diecinueve, diecisiete, quince, ______________________

Nombre: ______________________________ Fecha: ______________

10 ¿Cuántos años tienes?

You have just asked the following students their ages. Write their responses, using the cues provided.

MODELO: Ana / 13
Tengo trece años.

1. Roberto / 15

   ____

2. Marcos / 17

   ____

3. Claudia / 14

   ____

4. Elena / 16

   ____

5. Diego / 12

   ____

6. Marta / 18

   ____

11 ¿De dónde eres?

Imagine you are at a book convention where you ask several well-known Spanish-speaking writers where they are from. Following the model, write each response in the space provided.

MODELO: Isabel Allende / Chile
Soy de Chile.

1. Julia Álvarez / República Dominicana

   ____

2. Carlos Ruiz Zafón / España

   ____

3. Leonardo Padura / Cuba

   ____

4. Sandra Cisneros / Estados Unidos

   ____

5. Edgar Allan García / Ecuador

   ____

6. Sandra Scoppettone / Argentina

   ____

7. Mario Vargas Llosa / Perú

   ____

8. Esmeralda Santiago / Puerto Rico

   ____

Nombre: ______________________________ Fecha: ______________

12 Sí, soy de la capital

Match each question with the correct response.

1. ______ ¿Eres del Perú? A. Sí, soy de la capital, Bogotá.

2. ______ ¿Eres de Nicaragua? B. Sí, soy de la capital, Lima.

3. ______ ¿Eres de Colombia? C. Sí, soy de la capital, Santiago.

4. ______ ¿Eres de la República Dominicana? D. Sí, soy de la capital, Managua.

5. ______ ¿Eres de Chile? E. Sí, soy de la capital, Santo Domingo.

13 Soy de...

How would each person say where he or she is from? Following the model, write the response in the space provided. You might want to refer to the maps in the textbook.

MODELO: Soy de la Ciudad de México, la capital de México.

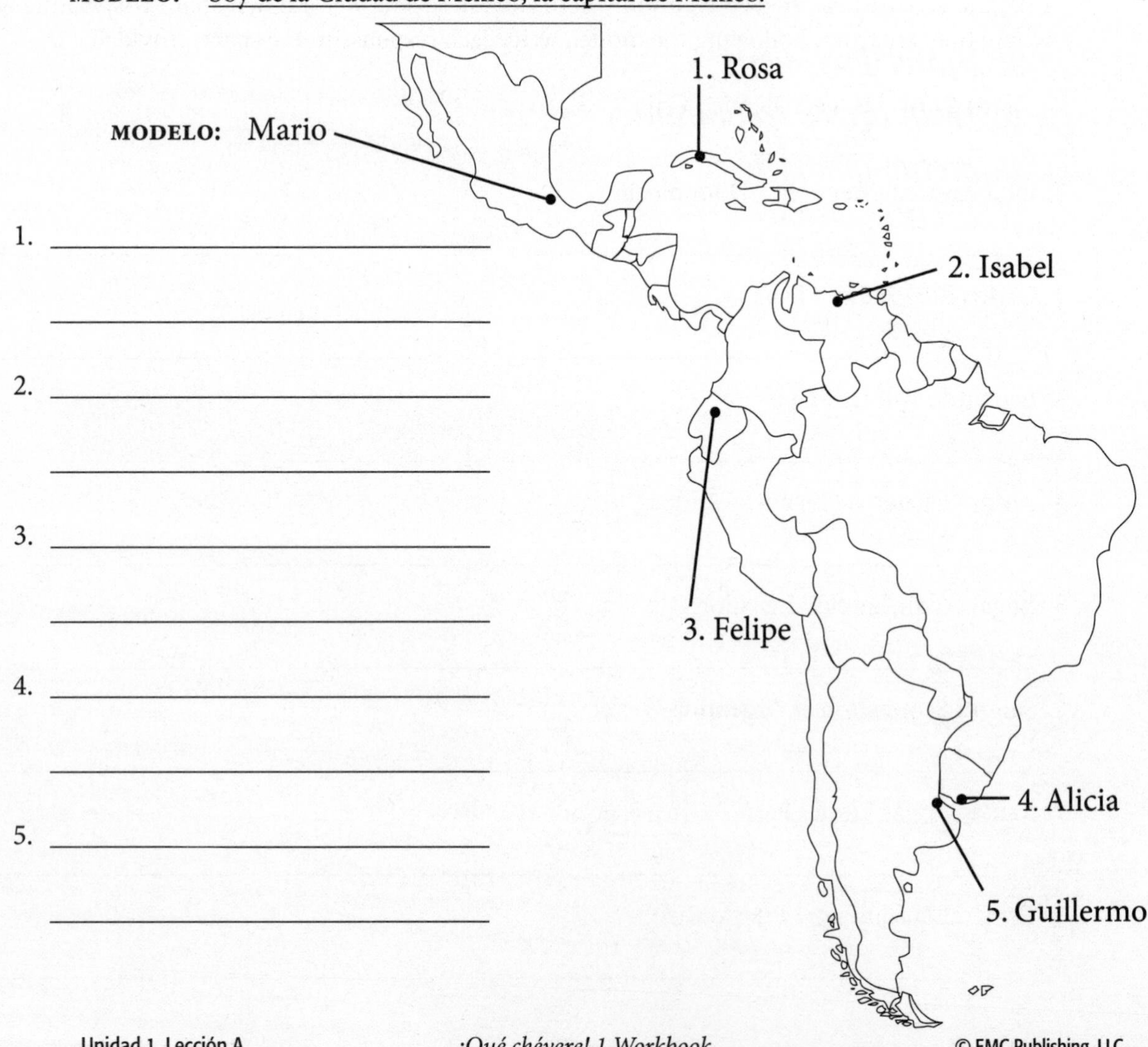

Nombre: ______________________________ Fecha: ______________

14 Los cognados

Look at the following website of a hotel. Find the Spanish words that are cognates to the list of English words below. Write each word in the corresponding space.

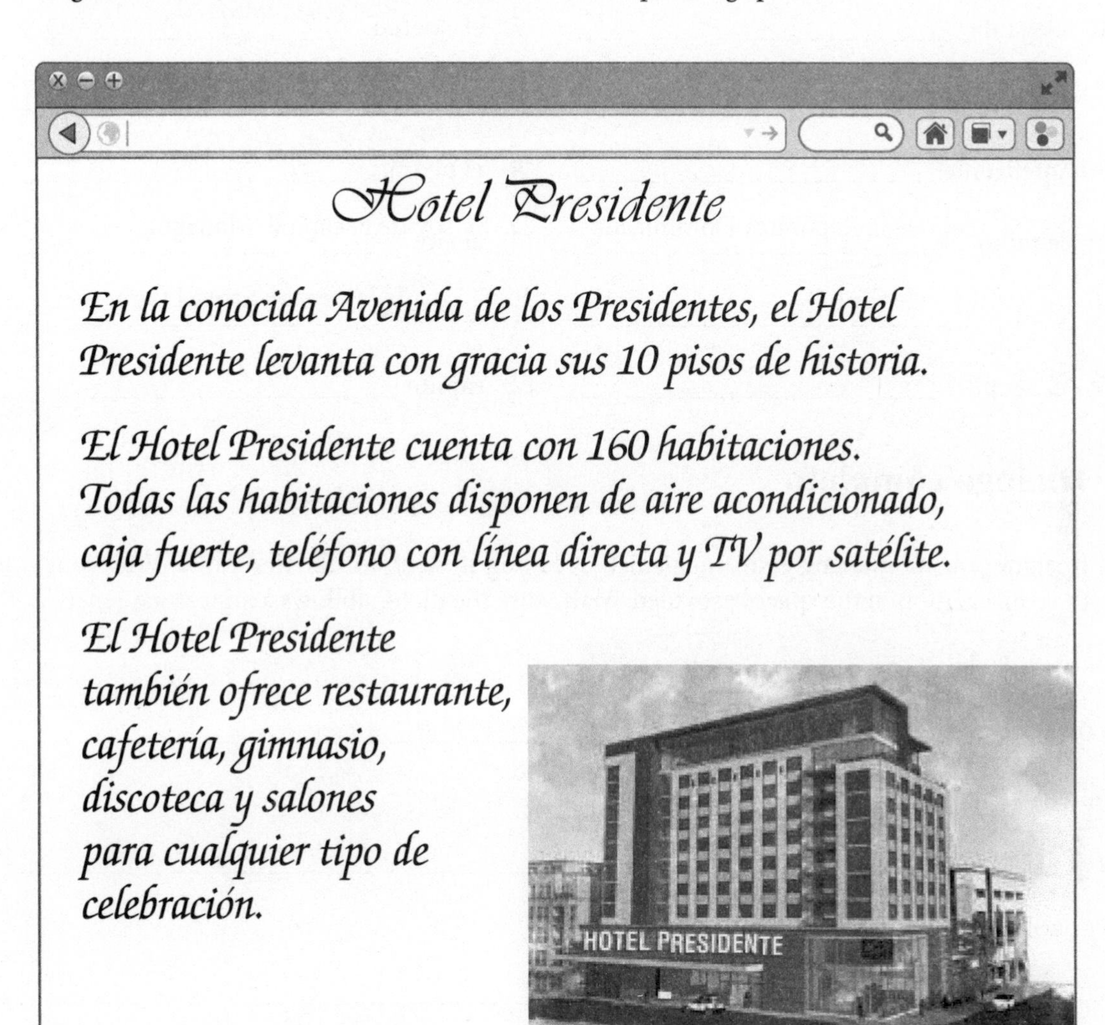

1. satellite ______________________
2. president ______________________
3. history ______________________
4. restaurant ______________________
5. celebration ______________________
6. telephone ______________________
7. air ______________________
8. cafeteria ______________________
9. direct ______________________
10. discotheque ______________________

Nombre: ______________________________ Fecha: ______________

15 Más cognados

Write the corresponding English word on the line that goes with the Spanish cognate.

1. elegante ______________
2. la biología ______________
3. inteligente ______________
4. la radio ______________
5. el carro ______________
6. el hospital ______________
7. el estéreo ______________
8. la historia ______________
9. el pijama ______________
10. el aire ______________
11. la mamá ______________
12. rápido ______________

16 Diálogo completo

Imagine you are meeting Pedro, a Spanish-speaking student, for the first time. Write your side of the conversation in the spaces provided. Make sure the dialog follows a logical sequence.

PEDRO: ¡Hola!

TÚ: ______________________________

PEDRO: ¿Cómo te llamas?

TÚ: ______________________________

PEDRO: Yo me llamo Pedro.

TÚ: ______________________________

PEDRO: Mucho gusto. ¿De dónde eres?

TÚ: ______________________________

PEDRO: No. Yo soy de El Salvador. ¿Cuántos años tienes?

TÚ: ______________________________

PEDRO: Yo tengo quince años.

TÚ: ______________________________

PEDRO: Adiós.

Nombre: ______________________ Fecha: __________

Lección B

1 ¿Qué tal?

Choose an appropriate response to each statement or question on the left.

		A	B
_______	1. Buenas tardes.	A. Hasta mañana.	B. Buenas tardes, señora.
_______	2. ¿Qué tal?	A. Bien, gracias.	B. Me llamo Carmen.
_______	3. Bien, ¿y tú?	A. Estoy regular.	B. Buenas noches.
_______	4. ¿Cómo están?	A. Buenas tardes.	B. Mal, muy mal.
_______	5. Hasta mañana.	A. Hasta pronto.	B. Buenos días.
_______	6. Adiós.	A. ¡Hola!	B. Hasta luego.
_______	7. Buenas noches.	A. Bien, ¿y tú?	B. Hasta mañana.

2 Hasta mañana

Complete each sentence logically with the appropriate word.

1. Buenos ______________________
2. ______________________ tardes.
3. ¿ ______________________ están Uds.?
4. Estoy mal, muy ______________________.
5. ¿ ______________________ tal?
6. Bien, ______________________
7. Buenas noches, ______________________ Torres.
8. ______________________ pronto, Juan.
9. ¿Cómo está ______________________, Sra. Chang?
10. ______________________ noches, Anita.

Nombre: ______________________ Fecha: ____________

3 Saludos y despedidas

Look at the pictures below and think of what the people might be saying to each other. Write the expressions that best fit the situation inside the speech bubbles.

4 Los saludos en el mundo hispano

Choose the greetings that are appropriate for each time of the day.

8:00 A.M.	Muy buenos días. Buenas. Buenos. Muy buenas. Hola.
2:30 P.M.	Hola. Buenos días. Buenas. Muy buenas. Muy buenas noches.
7:00 P.M.	Buenas tardes. Buenas. Buenas noches. Buenos. Muy buenas.

Nombre: ______________________________ Fecha: ______________

5 Saludos informales y formales

Are the following expressions appropriate to greet a friend or a person whom you would address with a title? Indicate which of the expressions are formal and which are informal. Write **F** for *formal* or **I** for *informal* in the space provided.

_______ 1. Muy buenos días.

_______ 2. ¿Qué tal?

_______ 3. ¿Cómo estás?

_______ 4. ¡Hola!

_______ 5. ¿Cómo está Ud.?

_______ 6. Buenas tardes.

6 Pronombres personales

How would you address the following people in Spanish? Write *tú, usted, ustedes, vosotros* or *vosotras* in the space provided.

1. Marta and Carlos, your friends from Mexico: ______________________
2. your little brother: ______________________
3. the parent of a classmate: ______________________
4. Victoria and Josefina, your friends from Spain: ______________________
5. the governor of your state: ______________________
6. Hugo and Armando, your friends from Spain: ______________________

Nombre: ______________________________ Fecha: ______________

7 Gente amable

Read the following situations. Choose the appropriate expression for each situation.

1. Mateo is having lunch with his friends. He is about to leave the gathering. What does he say?

   A. Con permiso B. Por favor

2. Lucía is at the mall. She asks people in a crowded area to let her pass by. What does she say?

   A. Perdón B. Con permiso

3. Marta is having a conversation with Pablo. Pablo interrupts her because he wants her to repeat her last sentence. What does he say?

   A. Gracias B. Perdón

4. Miguel asks Luis for a pen. What does he say to begin his request?

   A. Por favor B. Muchas gracias

5. Laura is walking on the street. She bumps into a lady. What does Laura say?

   A. Perdón B. Con permiso

6. Luis lends a pen to Miguel. What does Miguel say to Luis?

   A. Por favor B. Gracias

7. Juan goes to a job interview. How does he greet the interviewer?

   A. Buenas tardes. B. Hola, ¿qué tal?

8. Lisa runs into one of her teachers. How does she greet him?

   A. ¿Cómo está Ud.? B. ¿Qué hay?

9. Manuel meets his classmate at the school cafeteria. What does he say?

   A. Hola, ¿qué tal? B. ¿Cómo está Ud.?

10. Jaime joins his teenage friends at a birthday party. What does he say?

    A. Buenas tardes. B. ¿Qué hay?

Nombre: ______________________________ Fecha: ______________

8 Crucigrama

Complete the crossword puzzle with the correct spelling of the numbers provided.

Horizontales

1. 22
3. 100
4. 90
6. 60
7. 11
8. 40

Verticales

2. 70
3. 50
5. 30
6. 7

Nombre: ______________________________ Fecha: ______________

9 Cheques personales

Complete the following checks by writing out each sum.

Bancomer CHEQUE NO. 6654

PÁGUESE A LA
ORDEN DE I.N.E. $ 55.00

EN LETRAS LA
SUMA DE ______________________________ PESOS.

____

6654 7654 01001 007634521

Bancomer CHEQUE NO. 6655

PÁGUESE A LA
ORDEN DE Joaquín Sandoval $ 26.00

EN LETRAS LA
SUMA DE ______________________________ PESOS.

____

6654 7654 01001 007634521

Bancomer CHEQUE NO. 6656

PÁGUESE A LA
ORDEN DE Novedades $ 87.00

EN LETRAS LA
SUMA DE ______________________________ PESOS.

____

6654 7654 01001 007634521

Nombre: ______________________ Fecha: ______________

10 Números de teléfono

Write the telephone number of each restaurant given, following the model.

MODELO: Las Rejas: dieciséis, diez, ochenta y nueve

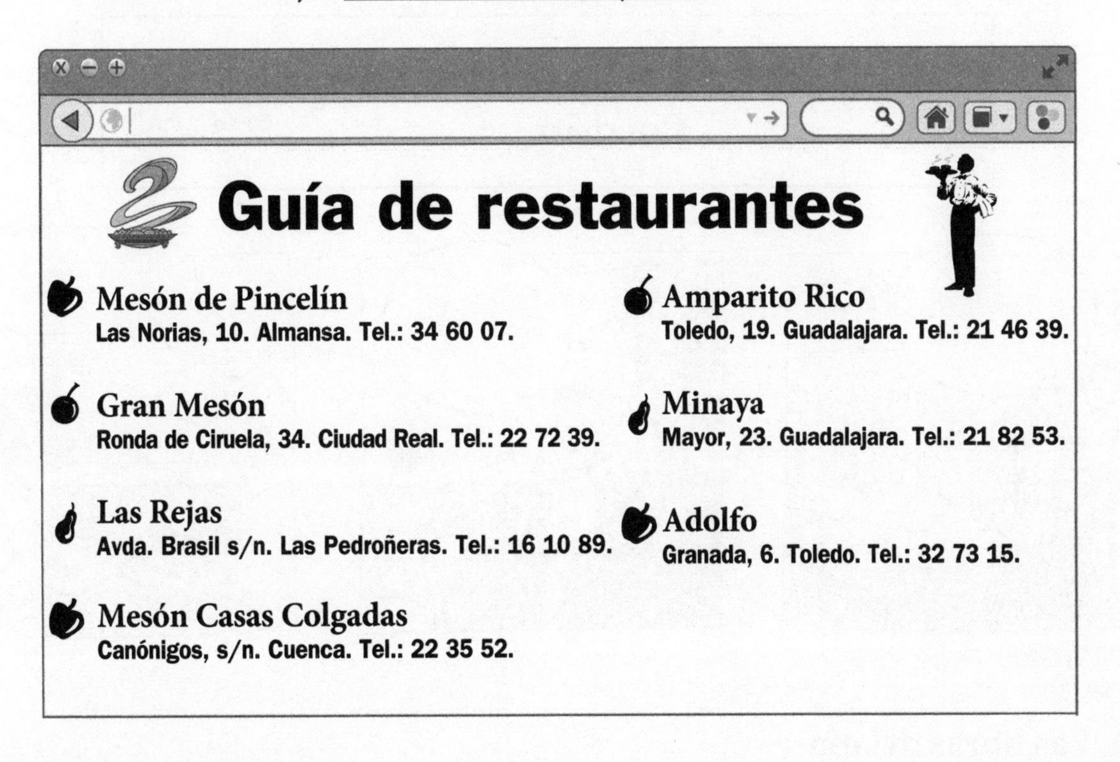

1. Mesón Casas Colgadas:

____

2. Adolfo:

____

3. Gran Mesón:

____

4. Amparito Rico:

____

5. Minaya:

____

6. Mesón de Pincelín:

____

Nombre: ______________________________ Fecha: ______________

11 Con cortesía

Look at the people in the drawing and imagine what they would say in each situation. Choose an appropriate expression from the word box and write it inside the speech bubble.

Con permiso.	Con mucho gusto.	Perdón.

1. 

2. 

3. 

12 Las horas del día

Sort the following times of day from earliest to latest. Number each line 1–8 to show the correct order.

_______ 1. Son las dos y media de la tarde.

_______ 2. Son las nueve de la noche.

_______ 3. Es mediodía.

_______ 4. Son las nueve menos veinte de la mañana.

_______ 5. Son las dos menos diez de la tarde.

_______ 6. Es medianoche.

_______ 7. Son las diez y cuarto de la noche.

_______ 8. Son las siete y diez de la mañana.

Nombre: ______________________________ Fecha: ______________

13 ¿Qué hora es?

What time is it? Look at each clock and write the correct time in the space provided.

1.  ______________________________

2. 

____

3.  ______________________________

4.  ______________________________

5. 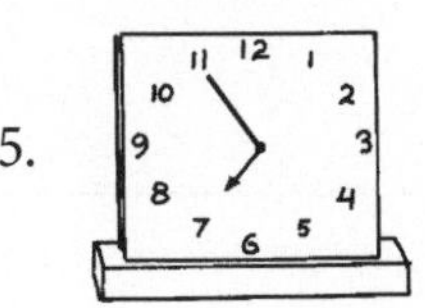 ______________________________

6. 

____

Nombre: ______________________________ Fecha: ______________

14 La geografía y la hora

Did you know that when it is seven o'clock in the morning in California, it is already four o'clock in the afternoon in Spain? Look at the following map showing various time zones. Use the clocks at the bottom of the map to help you answer each question.

MODELO: Es mediodía en España. ¿Y en Guinea Ecuatorial?
Es la una de la tarde en Guinea Ecuatorial.

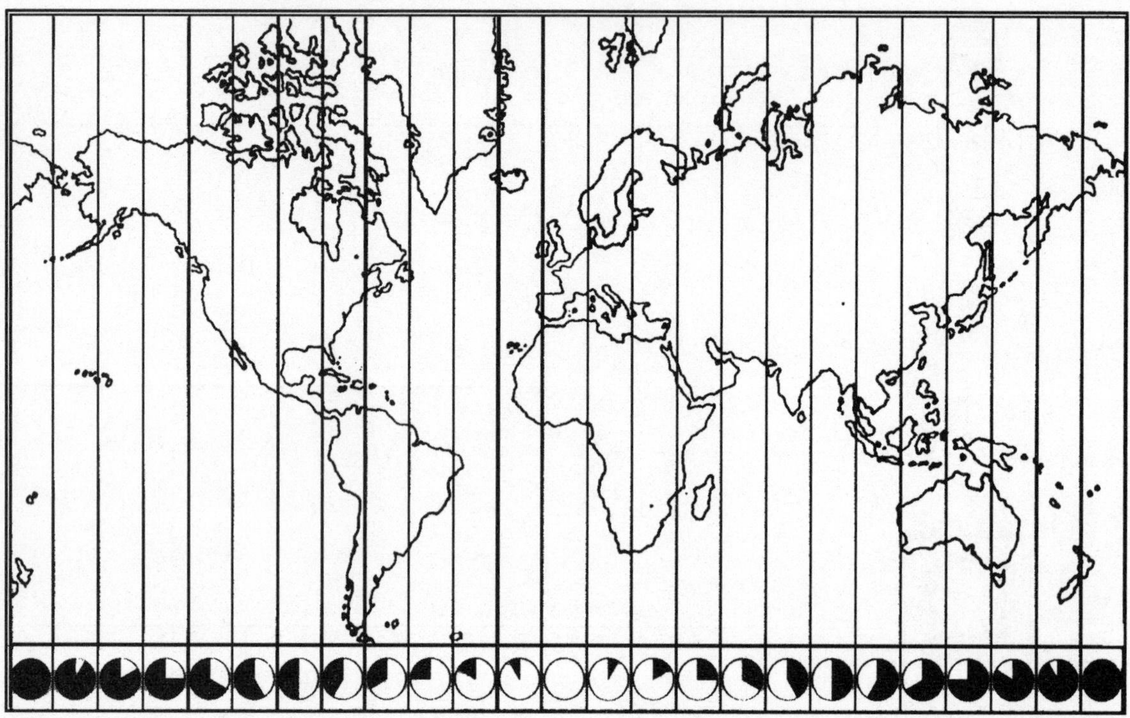

0:00 1:00 2:00 3:00 4:00 5:00 6:00 7:00 8:00 9:00 10:00 11:00 12:00 13:00 14:00 15:00 16:00 17:00 18:00 19:00 20:00 21:00 22:00 23:00 24:00

1. Es mediodía en España. ¿Y en Cuba?

____

2. Son las ocho de la mañana en México, D.F. ¿Y en Panamá?

____

3. Son las tres de la tarde en Chile. ¿Y en Guatemala?

____

4. Son las seis de la noche en la República Dominicana. ¿Y en Nicaragua?

____

5. Es medianoche en Colombia. ¿Y en España?

____

Nombre: ______________________ Fecha: ____________

Unidad 2

Lección A

1 Preguntas y respuestas

Match each question on the left with the most logical response on the right.

_______	1. ¿Quién es él?	A. Isabel Gómez.
_______	2. ¿Cómo se llama ella?	B. Me llamo Rafael.
_______	3. ¿De dónde son ellos?	C. Él es de Chicago.
_______	4. ¿Quién eres tú?	D. No, ellas son de México.
_______	5. ¿De dónde es él?	E. Él es Juan.
_______	6. ¿Son las chicas de aquí?	F. Ellos son de California.

2 ¿Quién es?

Diana and Alejo are at a party organized by the International Club. Complete the following conversation between them with the appropriate words.

ella eres llama dónde él quién es soy de

DIANA: Alejo, ¿(1)_______________ es?

ALEJO: ¿Quién? ¿Ella?

DIANA: No, (2)_______________.

ALEJO: Se (3)_______________ Ricardo.

DIANA: ¿De (4)_______________ es él?

ALEJO: Es (5)_______________ Venezuela.

DIANA: ¿Y (6)_______________?

ALEJO: Laura (7)_______________ de Puerto Rico.

DIANA: ¿Y tú, Alejo? ¿De dónde (8)_______________?

ALEJO: Yo (9)_______________ de Nicaragua.

Nombre: ______________________________ Fecha: ____________

3 Pronombres personales

Rewrite the following sentences, replacing the underlined words with an appropriate subject pronoun.

Modelo: Joaquín y yo somos de Texas.
Nosotros somos de Texas.

1. María González es de la Florida.

____

2. El señor y la señora López son de California.

____

3. Jorge es de la República Dominicana.

____

4. Magdalena y Pilar son de Arizona.

____

5. Miguel y yo somos de los Estados Unidos.

____

6. Marcos y Ronaldo son de Nueva York.

____

7. Me llamo Luisa. Olga y yo somos de Cuba.

____

8. El Sr. Morales es de Puerto Rico.

____

9. La señora Núñez y la señorita Chávez son de El Paso.

____

10. Tú y yo somos de aquí.

____

Nombre: ______________________________ Fecha: ______________

4 ¿De dónde son?

Write six sentences, telling where the following people are from.

MODELO: Alma es de Venezuela.

1. ______________________________
2. ______________________________
3. ______________________________
4. ______________________________
5. ______________________________
6. ______________________________

Nombre: ______________________ Fecha: ____________

5 No

Your friend is mistaken about the place of origin of the following famous people. Make the statements negative and then tell where they are from, using the cues provided.

MODELO: Antonio Banderas es de México. (España)
Antonio Banderas no es de México. Es de España.

1. Celia Cruz es de Puerto Rico. (Cuba)

 ____

2. Frida Kahlo y Diego Rivera son de Argentina. (México)

 ____

3. Alex Rodríguez es de California. (Nueva York)

 ____

4. Rigoberta Menchú es de Chile. (Guatemala)

 ____

5. Shakira y Juanes son de España. (Colombia)

 ____

6 A escribir

Use an item from each column to write five sentences.

yo	es	de México
Ud.	soy	de Nueva York
Juan y Ana	eres	de San Antonio
nosotros	son	de Puerto Rico
tú	somos	de los Estados Unidos

1. ______________________________
2. ______________________________
3. ______________________________
4. ______________________________
5. ______________________________

Nombre: ______________________________ Fecha: ______________

7 El español en los Estados Unidos

Choose the words that have been borrowed from Spanish.

patio burrito culture jazz condor banana language

tornado cumbia community demand salsa apple

8 El idioma español y su cultura

Decide whether each of the following statements about Hispanic culture in the United States is *cierto* (true) or *falso* (false). Write **C** or **F** in the space provided.

______ 1. Words like *cafeteria*, *taco*, and *mesa* are of Spanish origin.

______ 2. Rhythms like *salsa*, *merengue*, and *cumbia* are American rhythms.

______ 3. The cowboy tradition in America has its roots in Mexico and Spain.

______ 4. *San Agustín* is the original name of the city currently located in Florida.

______ 5. Names like Los Angeles, Monterey, and Grand Canyon are of English origin.

______ 6. Currently, the Hispanic population in the United States is decreasing.

Nombre: ______________________________ Fecha: ______________

9 ¿Cómo se dice?

Match each question on the left with the correct response on the right.

_______	1. ¿Cómo se dice *backpack?*	A.	Quiere decir *notebook.*
_______	2. ¿Cómo se dice *pencil?*	B.	Se dice *mochila.*
_______	3. ¿Qué quiere decir *cuaderno?*	C.	Se dice *ventana.*
_______	4. ¿Cómo se dice *window?*	D.	Quiere decir *chair.*
_______	5. ¿Qué quiere decir *marcador?*	E.	Quiere decir *marker.*
_______	6. ¿Qué quiere decir *silla?*	F.	Se dice *lápiz.*

10 ¿Quién es?

Look at the drawing and read the questions. Write the name of the person in the space provided.

Sr. Vargas

Marta

Alejandro

Sr. Castro

Silvia

Mauricio

1. ¿Quién es la chica con el libro? ______________________________
2. ¿Quién es el señor con el bolígrafo? ______________________________
3. ¿Quién es el chico con el papel? ______________________________
4. ¿Quién es el señor con el periódico? ______________________________
5. ¿Quién es la chica con la mochila? ______________________________
6. ¿Quién es el chico con el lápiz? ______________________________

Nombre: ______________________________ Fecha: ______________

11 Crucigrama

Complete the following crossword puzzle with the Spanish words that correspond to the pictures.

Horizontales

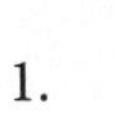
1. 

3. 

5.

7. 

9. 

10. 

Verticales

2. 

4. 

6. 

7. 

8. 

Nombre: ______________________________ Fecha: ______________

12 Artículos definidos

Write *el, la, los* or *las* in the space provided.

MODELO: el cuaderno

1. ______ bolígrafo
2. ______ amigas
3. ______ profesor
4. ______ libros
5. ______ marcador
6. ______ mochilas
7. ______ reloj
8. ______ periódicos
9. ______ paredes
10. ______ silla
11. ______ chicas
12. ______ borrador

13 Identifica

Skim the following advertisement to identify five nouns. Write the nouns in the space provided and next to each one, write the letter **M** for masculine or **F** for feminine. Use the definite articles and the endings of the nouns as clues.

MODELO: respuesta—F

RENAULT Scénic 2

Todo comenzó el día en que me compré el Scénic 2. Apenas me subí sentí el confort de un auto distinto. La posición de manejo sobreelevada, la gran visibilidad, la agilidad, la respuesta de su motor 2.0 L de 140 cv y la funcionalidad de todos sus comandos. Los asientos traseros individuales, el gran espacio interior y sobre todo la seguridad. Sentí que encontré otro espacio para mi vida, mi nueva vida. www.scenic2.com.ar

Salí, vivilo todo.

1. ______________________________
2. ______________________________
3. ______________________________
4. ______________________________
5. ______________________________

Nombre: ______________________________ Fecha: ______________

14 Plurales

Change the following words to the plural form.

MODELO: un libro → unos libros

1. un papel → ______________________
2. un lápiz → ______________________
3. una mochila → ______________________
4. una revista → ______________________
5. un marcador → ______________________
6. una profesora → ______________________

15 ¿Qué son?

Identify the illustrated objects, following the model.

MODELO:  Es una regla.

1.  ______________________
2.  ______________________
3. ______________________
4.  ______________________
5. 

____

Nombre: ______________________________ Fecha: ______________

16 ¿Qué hay en la clase?

For each item listed, say whether it is found in your classroom. If it is, include how many. Follow the model.

MODELO: mapa: Hay dos mapas. / No hay un mapa.

1. cesto de papeles: ______________________________
2. estudiante: ______________________________
3. puerta: ______________________________
4. ventana: ______________________________
5. silla: ______________________________
6. pared: ______________________________
7. sacapuntas: ______________________________
8. reloj: ______________________________
9. pizarra: ______________________________
10. pupitre: ______________________________

17 Las notas

Use the grading scale to convert the following grades for your Mexican pen pal. Write S, EX, MB, B, NM or D in the space provided.

______ 1. 90% en matemáticas

______ 2. 60% en historia

______ 3. 100% en arte

______ 4. 40% en música

______ 5. 80% en español

______ 6. 50% en biología

Escala	
10	Superior (S)
9	Excelente (EX)
8	Muy Bueno (MB)
7–6	Bueno (B)
5	Necesita Mejorar (NM)
4–0	Deficiente (D)

Nombre: ______________________ Fecha: ______________

18 ¿Qué tienes en la mochila?

Make a list of the school supplies you carry in your backpack. Be sure to include the appropriate indefinite articles.

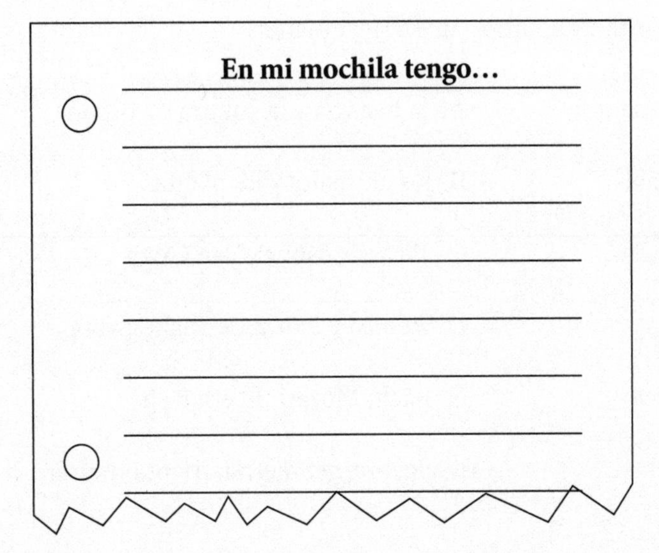

Nombre: ______________________________ Fecha: ______________

Lección B

1 ¿Qué clase es?

Match each class with its appropriate subject matter.

_______	1. matemáticas	A. la historia y la cultura de España
_______	2. español	B. los animales y las plantas
_______	3. biología	C. Picasso, Monet, Van Gogh
_______	4. arte	D. *Romeo y Julieta* de Shakespeare
_______	5. música	E. Bach, Mozart, Beethoven
_______	6. inglés	F. álgebra, geometría, trigonometría

2 Siete colores

In the word-square puzzle, find and circle seven names of colors. The words may read horizontally, vertically or diagonally.

S	N	V	Y	R	S	A	W	A	T
T	A	E	E	O	D	M	Z	D	E
R	E	R	G	G	T	A	X	U	D
O	F	D	O	R	A	R	A	S	L
J	E	E	C	I	O	I	R	O	S
O	R	B	L	S	P	L	E	L	L
Q	J	E	L	I	U	L	G	M	V
U	B	L	A	N	C	O	H	A	R

Nombre: ______________________________ Fecha: ______________

3 ¿Sí o no?

Read the statements and decide whether they are true or false, based on Elena's class schedule. If the statement is true, write *sí* in the space provided. If it is false, write *no*.

El horario de clases de Elena					
Hora	**Lunes**	**Martes**	**Miércoles**	**Jueves**	**Viernes**
8:00 A.M.	matemáticas	matemáticas	matemáticas	matemáticas	matemáticas
8:50 A.M.	español	español	español	español	español
10:40 A.M.	historia	historia	historia	historia	historia
11:45 A.M.	inglés	computación	inglés	computación	inglés
12:35 A.M.	almuerzo	almuerzo	almuerzo	almuerzo	almuerzo
1:45 P.M.	biología	biología	biología	biología	biología
2:35 P.M.	arte	música	arte	música	arte

________ 1. Elena tiene seis clases en un día.

________ 2. La clase de matemáticas es a las ocho de la mañana.

________ 3. La clase de español es a las diez y cuarenta de la mañana.

________ 4. Hay clase de inglés martes y jueves a las doce menos cuarto.

________ 5. No hay clase de música los lunes, miércoles y viernes.

________ 6. El almuerzo es a la una y cuarenta y cinco de la tarde.

________ 7. Elena tiene clase de biología a las dos menos cuarto.

________ 8. La clase de computación es a las doce menos cuarto los martes y los jueves.

________ 9. Hay clase de historia los lunes, miércoles y viernes a las nueve menos diez de la mañana.

________ 10. Las clases de Elena terminan a la una y treinta y cinco de la tarde.

Nombre: ______________________________ Fecha: ______________

4 Sustantivos y adjetivos

For each sentence, underline the noun and circle the adjective. Then, check the appropriate columns to indicate whether it is masculine or feminine and singular or plural. Follow the model.

	Masculine	Feminine	Singular	Plural
MODELO: Daniel lleva una camiseta nueva.		√	√	
1. Sergio es un estudiante nuevo.				
2. La chica nueva es de México.				
3. Los zapatos son negros.				
4. Las paredes son blancas.				
5. Ella lleva una blusa amarilla.				
6. Necesito unos lápices rojos.				

5 La ropa y los colores

Maricela is talking on her cell phone, describing what people are wearing to the party. Complete her statements with the correct form of the adjective in parenthesis. Be sure the adjective agrees in gender and number with the noun it describes.

MODELO: Arturo lleva una camiseta roja. (rojo)

1. Nuria y Pilar llevan unas blusas ____________________. (blanco)
2. Mi amigo Pepe lleva unos calcetines ________________________. (rojo)
3. Mabel lleva una falda ____________________________. (amarillo)
4. Mauricio lleva unos zapatos ________________________. (gris)
5. Dos chicos llevan unos jeans ____________________________. (negro)
6. Los pantalones de Selena son ____________________________. (verde)
7. Yo llevo pantalones ______________________. Son ____________________. (azul, nuevo)

Nombre: ______________________________ Fecha: ______________

6 En el colegio

Complete each sentence logically with the appropriate verb form. You will need to use one verb twice.

hablar llevar necesitar terminar estudiar

MODELO: La señora Sánchez habla inglés y español.

1. Jaime y yo ______________________ papel para la clase de arte.
2. Los estudiantes ______________________ pantalones grises y camisas blancas.
3. La clase de historia ______________________ al mediodía.
4. ¿______________________ tú computación?
5. Yo ______________________ en el Colegio Cervantes.
6. Gabriela ______________________ español muy bien.

Nombre: ______________________________ Fecha: ______________

7 ¿Qué necesitan?

Write a sentence telling what the person(s) need(s). Use the pictures as clues and the correct forms of the verb *necesitar* and the adjective *nuevo*. Follow the model.

MODELO:  Sara

Sara necesita un lápiz nuevo.

1.  nosotros

____

2. Pedro

____

3.  Ana y Lupe

____

4.  yo

____

5.  Ernesto

____

6.  tú

____

Nombre: ______________________ Fecha: ______________

8 Radio Nacional

Answer the questions based on the following schedule for an Argentinian radio station. Note that in Argentina, the 24-hour clock is used. In this system, 14.00 is the same as two o'clock in the afternoon.

MODELO: ¿A qué hora es "De Segovia a…"?
Es a las nueve de la noche.

FM Música

Radio Nacional

6.00: La mañana de Radio Nacional.
9.00: El órgano (A. Gómez).
10.00: Cuadro de situación (S. Crivelli).
11.00: Aproximación a la ópera (Juan Carlos Montero).
13.00: Bailando sobre el Titanic.
14.00: Intimidad con la música.
16.00: Teatro Cervantes.
16.30: Operamante (C. Ratier).
20.00: Discoteca F. M. 96.7
21.00: De Segovia a... con S. Domínguez.
22.00: España y su música (O. Monzo).
23.00: Discoteca.
24.00: Clásicos Siglo XX, con Alicia Terzián.

1. ¿A qué hora es "El órgano"?

   ____

2. ¿A qué hora es "Bailando sobre el Titanic"?

   ____

3. ¿A qué hora termina el Teatro Cervantes?

   ____

4. ¿A qué hora es "España y su música"?

   ____

5. ¿Qué hay a las once de la noche?

   ____

6. ¿A qué hora es "Clásicos Siglo XX"?

   ____

Nombre: ____ Fecha: ________________

9 La cultura y la educación hispana

Choose the correct completion for each statement about culture and education in Spanish-speaking ountries.

1. You can explore coral reefs in…

   A. Honduras. B. Chile.

2. In… you can visit pyramids and jungles.

   A. Chile B. México

3. You can visit the driest desert in the world in…

   A. México. B. Chile.

4. Joining a student exchange program can be a… experience.

   A. very fulfilling B. barely fulfilling

5. In a student exchange program, you live…

   A. at a hotel. B. with a family.

6. If you host an exchange student in your home…

   A. only she benefits. B. you both benefit.

10 Los colegios en el mundo hispano

Read the following statements. Based on what you have learned about schools in Spanish-speaking countries, decide whether the statements refer to their schools or to our schools. Write *theirs* or *ours* in the space provided.

______ 1. Students attend class all day.

______ 2. Schools offer a morning and an afternoon shift.

______ 3. Students usually learn a second language in elementary school.

______ 4. Soccer is the most popular sport in gym class.

______ 5. The curriculum in high school is very demanding.

______ 6. There are many extracurricular activities for students.

Nombre: ______________________________ Fecha: ______________

11 La computadora

Identify the parts of the computer in the following illustration.

12 Números y direcciones

Your friend is interested in staying at Hotel San Roque, a small hotel in Spain. Use the information in this magazine clipping to answer his questions.

A. DIRECCIÓN: Esteban de Ponte, 32. 38450, Garachico. Tenerife. Tel.: 922 13 34 35. Fax: 922 13 34 06. Web: www.hotelsanroque.com E-mail: info@hotelsanroque.com **B.** ACCESOS: autopista T1 hasta el Puerto de la Cruz. De ahí, tomar la C-820 hasta Icod de los Vinos y Garachico. En el mismo Garachico, seguir indicaciones hasta el hotel, que está a unos 25 kilometros del Puerto de la Cruz. **C.** CATEGORÍA: tres estrellas. **D.** INSTALACIONES: nueve habitaciones dobles, siete dúplex, dos *junior suites* y dos *suites* con baño completo, caja fuerte, minibar, TV, video y equipo de música, sala de lectura y salón social, patio-bar, sauna, solario y piscina climatizada. **E.** GASTRONOMÍA: cocina de mercado, asesorada por el restaurante Celler de Can Roca en Girona. **F.** PRECIOS: doble estándar: 175 €; dúplex: 187 €; *junior suite*: 225 €; *suite*: 247 €. Desayuno incluido.

1. ¿Cuál es el número de teléfono? ______________________________
2. ¿Cuál es la dirección de correo electrónico? ______________________________
3. ¿Cuál es la dirección de Internet? ______________________________
4. ¿Cuál es el número de fax? ______________________________

Nombre: ______________________________ Fecha: ______________

13 El verbo *estar*

Complete the following e-mail message with the correct forms of the verb *estar*.

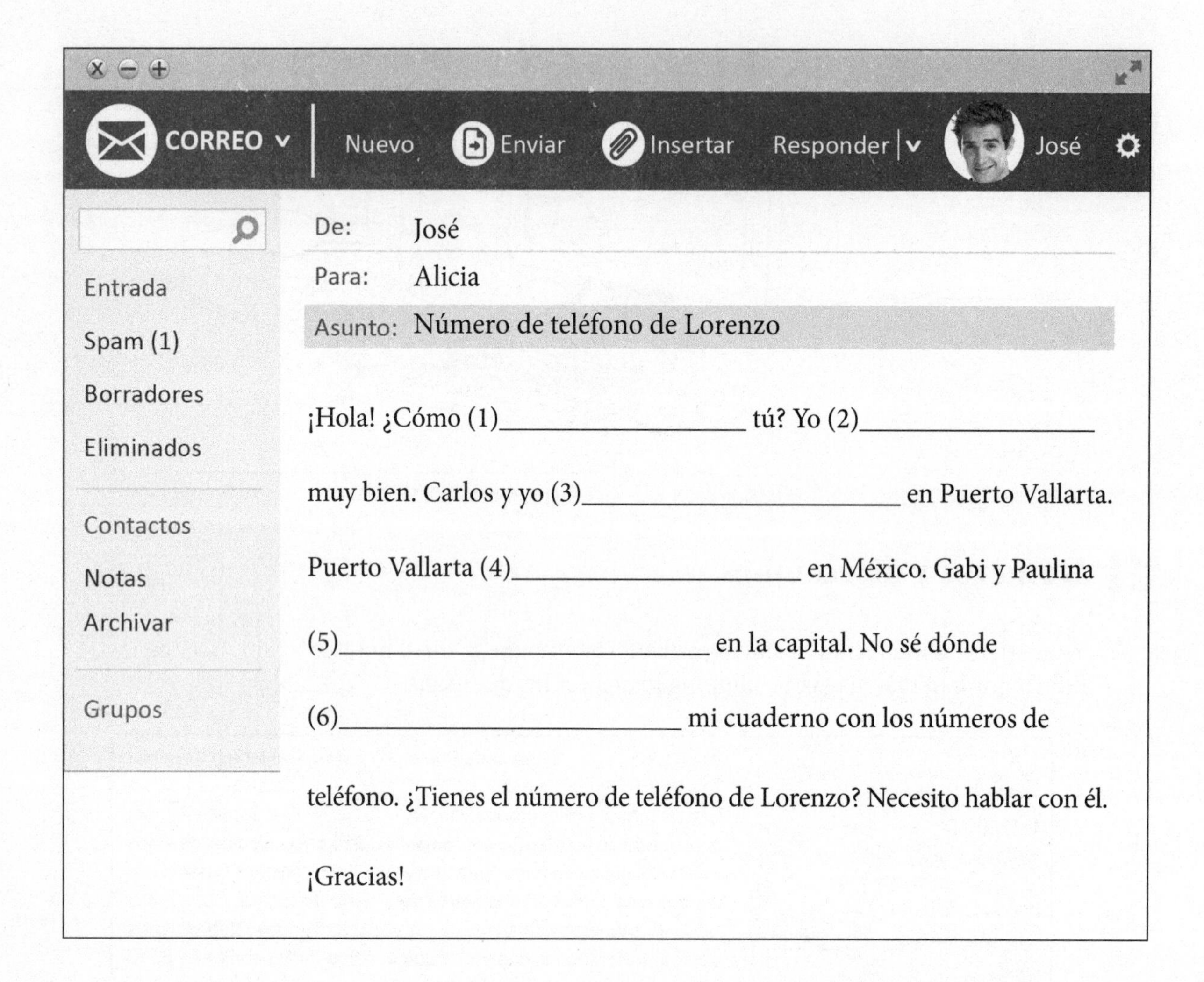

Nombre: ______________________________ Fecha: ______________

14 ¿Dónde está?

Look at the illustration of José's bedroom and answer the questions that follow.

MODELO: ¿Dónde está el reloj?
El reloj está en la pared.

1. ¿Dónde está la computadora?

____

2. ¿Dónde está la mochila?

____

3. ¿Dónde está el mapa de los Estados Unidos?

____

4. ¿Dónde están los libros?

____

5. ¿Dónde están los papeles?

____

6. ¿Dónde está el disco compacto?

____

Nombre: ______________________________ Fecha: ______________

15 Diálogo completo

The school newspaper is going to write an article about a school in Mexico, but the reporter only recorded the answers of the student he interviewed. As the editor, write logical questions in the spaces provided.

1. ______________________________

   Me llamo Juan Carlos Macedo Olivas.

2. ______________________________

   Mi correo electrónico es JCOlivas@telecom.mex.

3. ______________________________

   Es el 9-76-13-32.

4. ______________________________

   Mi colegio se llama Preparatoria Nevada.

5. ______________________________

   Está en Guadalajara, México.

6. ______________________________

   Tengo siete clases en un día.

7. ______________________________

   Terminan a las tres de la tarde.

8. ______________________________

   Sí, mañana hay un examen de historia.

9. ______________________________

   El examen es a las diez y media de la mañana.

10. ______________________________

    Allí está. Sobre la mesa.

Nombre: ______________________________ Fecha: ____________

Unidad 3

Lección A

1 ¿Dónde están?

Where is everyone? Match the phrases in English on the left with the appropriate phrase in Spanish on the right. Write the letter of your choice in the space provided.

______	1. Jorge is depositing a check.	A.	Está en el cine.
______	2. Margarita is getting her teeth cleaned.	B.	Está en el parque.
______	3. Laura is checking out a book.	C.	Está en el banco.
______	4. Gustavo is watching a movie.	D.	Está en el médico.
______	5. Guillermo is jogging.	E.	Está en el dentista.
______	6. Sr. López is teaching biology.	F.	Está en el hotel.
______	7. Sra. Sainz is resting after a long trip.	G.	Está en la escuela.
______	8. Josefina is getting a flu shot.	H.	Está en la biblioteca.

2 ¡Vamos!

Roberto and Marta are at the park when Rocío shows up. Complete the conversation between them with the appropriate words.

encantada	quiero	simpática	vamos	mañana
por qué	presento	mucho gusto	cuándo	fiesta

MARTA: Allí está mi amiga Rocío. Es una chica (1)________________. ¡Hola, Rocío!

ROCÍO: ¡Hola!

MARTA: Rocío, te (2)________________ a Roberto.

ROBERTO: (3)________________.

ROCÍO: (4)________________. Saben, hay una (5)________________ en la escuela. ¿(6)________________ no vamos?

MARTA: ¿(7)________________ es?

ROCÍO: Es (8)________________ a las siete de la noche.

ROBERTO: Yo (9)________________ ir.

MARTA: ¡(10)________________!

Nombre: ______________________________ Fecha: ______________

3 En la fiesta

At a party, how would you introduce the guests? Complete the following introductions logically with the words *te*, *le* or *les*.

MODELO: Eugenio, te presento a mi amiga Anabel.

1. Sr. y Sra. Ortega, __________ presento a la profesora de arte.
2. Arturo, __________ presento a Sergio, el amigo de Alma.
3. Profesora Prieto, __________ presento a Vero y Carla.
4. Blanca y Ángela, __________ presento a Hugo y Raúl.
5. Miguel, __________ presento al señor Gómez, mi profesor de español.
6. Don Rodrigo, __________ presento a mi amiga Lupe.
7. Vero y Carla, __________ presento a doña Violeta.
8. Señor Gómez, __________ presento a Sergio y Alma.
9. Gabi, __________ presento al amigo de doña Violeta.
10. Hugo y Raúl, __________ presento a don Rodrigo.

4 Más presentaciones

Combine elements from each column to write five introductions. Be sure to use contractions when necessary.

MODELO: Clara, te presento al señor Portillo.

Clara	te presento a	mis amigos Diego y Tomás
Srta. Guzmán	le presento a	el profesor de computación
Enrique	les presento a	el señor Portillo
don Humberto		doña Esperanza
Sr. y Sra. Ramírez		el estudiante de Honduras
Daniel y Nicolás		el amigo de Fernando

1. ______________________________
2. ______________________________
3. ______________________________
4. ______________________________
5. ______________________________

Nombre: ________________________________ Fecha: ______________

5 Mucho gusto

In the following drawing, Silvia is introducing José to the math teacher, Sr. Torres. Complete the speech bubbles with appropriate expressions.

6 Preguntas

Complete the following questions with the appropriate question words.

1. ¿________________ te llamas?
2. ¿________________ es tu dirección de correo electrónico?
3. ¿________________ quiere decir la palabra *escuela*?
4. ¿________________ van al restaurante?
5. ¿________________ es la fiesta de Yolanda?
6. ¿________________ están mis libros de inglés?
7. ¿________________ no vamos al cine mañana?
8. ¿________________ escritorios hay en la oficina?

Nombre: ______________________________ Fecha: ______________

7 Más preguntas

Unscramble the words and write complete, logical questions.

MODELO: ¿? / en / el parque / Sofía / camina
¿Camina Sofía en el parque?

1. ¿? / el amigo / simpático / de / verdad / Beatriz / es

____

2. ¿? / Andrés / Jaime / van / a / y / la fiesta

____

3. ¿? / sabe / la fiesta / Julia / cuándo / es

____

4. ¿? / es / mañana / no / la fiesta

____

5. ¿? / Uds. / la biblioteca / van / a

____

6. ¿? / las dos / la clase / termina / a

____

Nombre: ______________________ Fecha: ______________

8 Viaje a Machu Picchu

A travel agency called Atalaya Turismo is planning a trip *(un viaje)* to the ruins of Machu Picchu in Peru. Look at the advertisement and write questions about the trip. Use the answers provided to help you write logical questions for each answer.

1. ______________________

El viaje *(trip)* es el 29 de noviembre.

2. ______________________

El viaje es de siete días.

3. ______________________

El hotel se llama Machu Picchu Inn.

4. ______________________

Van en tren panorámico.

5. ______________________

No, no van a Arequipa.

6. ______________________

El número de teléfono de Atalaya Turismo es el 4312-5784.

Nombre: ______________________________ Fecha: ______________

9 De visita en la Ciudad de México

What things and places could you see or visit in Mexico City? Match the name of the place in Spanish on the left with the appropriate description in English on the right. Write the correct letter in the space provided.

_____	1. el Zócalo	A.	the seat of government of Mexico
_____	2. la Plaza de la Constitución	B.	an amusement park
_____	3. el Palacio Nacional	C.	Mexico City's main square
_____	4. la Catedral Metropolitana	D.	an ancient cathedral
_____	5. Chapultepec	E.	the official name for *el Zócalo*
_____	6. el parque de atracciones	F.	a very large park

Nombre: ______________________ Fecha: ______________

10 Sopa de letras

In the word-square find and circle ten modes of transportation in Spanish. The words may read vertically, horizontally or diagonally.

W	E	C	A	M	I	Ó	N	E	R	T	Ó
T	Á	L	A	U	M	V	T	U	Z	L	S
B	P	B	A	R	C	O	Y	R	I	X	L
N	Z	I	Y	F	R	M	A	Ó	E	B	M
T	T	C	A	U	T	O	B	Ú	S	N	U
Í	D	I	F	V	U	T	D	O	O	P	L
V	S	C	Y	B	I	O	A	M	M	O	J
Q	Ú	L	Á	N	N	Ó	W	X	A	K	L
U	C	E	T	G	H	E	N	E	I	O	N
M	E	T	R	O	R	M	W	Y	U	I	D
R	S	A	N	S	P	Ó	R	T	A	B	É

11 ¿Cómo vamos?

How would you travel from one place to another? Write a mode of transportation that would make sense. In most cases, there is more than one possible answer.

MODELO: ¿De México, D.F. a Jalisco? en autobús

1. ¿De Chicago a México, D.F.? ______________________
2. ¿De Cancún a Cozumel? ______________________
3. ¿De México, D.F. a Puebla? ______________________
4. ¿Del Zócalo a Chapultepec? ______________________
5. ¿De la escuela al cine? ______________________
6. ¿Del hotel a un restaurante cerca? ______________________

Nombre: ______________________________ Fecha: ______________

12 Un mensaje electrónico

Complete the following e-mail with the correct forms of the verb *ir*.

CORREO Nuevo Enviar Insertar Responder Natalia

Entrada
Spam (1)
Borradores
Eliminados
Contactos
Notas
Archivar
Grupos

De: Natalia
Para: Irene
Asunto: Fiesta

¡Hola, Irene!

Sabes, Félix y yo no (1)________________ a la fiesta mañana. Félix no (2)________________ porque él y un amigo (3)________________ al cine. Yo no (4)________________ porque no tengo transporte y la fiesta está lejos. Iván tampoco (5)________________ porque (6)________________ al dentista. Rebeca y Antonio sí (7)________________. ¿Y tú? ¿(8)________________ a la fiesta? ¿Cómo (9)____________ tú? ¿Tienes transporte? ¿(10)________________ tú y yo juntas (*together*)?

Hasta luego,

Natalia

Nombre: ______________________________ Fecha: ______________

13 ¿Quiénes van?

Complete the sentences with the appropriate subjects from the list.

yo tú vosotras mis amigos Leonardo nosotros

1. ______________ van a la escuela a pie.
2. ______________ vais al cine, ¿verdad?
3. ______________ no va a la biblioteca con Manuel.
4. ______________ voy al banco en taxi.
5. ______________ no vamos a la fiesta de Raquel.
6. ______________ vas a la oficina a las ocho, ¿verdad?

14 ¿Cómo van?

Write complete sentences saying how the following people get to their workplaces.

MODELO: Federico  Federico va en metro.

1. Olga y Maira 

____

____

2. el Sr. Barrientos 

____

____

3. yo 

____

____

4. Rubén 

____

____

5. tú 

____

____

6. Graciela 

____

____

Nombre: ______________________ Fecha: __________

15 ¿Adónde y a qué hora van?

Combine elements from each column to write six complete sentences about where people are going and at what time. Add any necessary words and make changes as needed.

MODELO: Eduardo va a la médica a las dos de la tarde.

Eduardo	escuela	8:15 A.M.
mis amigos	cine	10:00 A.M.
tú	banco	12:00 P.M.
el estudiante nuevo	fiesta	2:00 P.M.
don Ignacio	parque	4:30 P.M.
Alicia y Gloria	médica	6:45 P.M.
Juan y yo	biblioteca	7:30 P.M.
la profesora	restaurante	8:45 P.M.

1. ______________________________

2. ______________________________

3. ______________________________

4. ______________________________

5. ______________________________

6. ______________________________

Nombre: ______________________ Fecha: ______________

16 Playa del Carmen

Some of your friends are thinking of going to Playa del Carmen, a popular beach in Mexico. They would like more information about the place: how to get there, is it close to Cancún, a name of a fantastic hotel, what is in Xcaret, etc. Prepare a list of six to eight questions in Spanish to ask a local Mexican travel agency. If you would like, search the Internet for the answers to your questions.

____

____

____

____

____

____

____

____

____

____

Nombre: ______________________________ Fecha: ______________

Lección B

1 Crucigrama

Complete the following crossword puzzle with words related to downtown.

Horizontales

5. La oficina está en un _______ grande.
6. Hay muchos edificios en el _______.
7. El concierto de rock va a ser en la _____.
8. Una ______ es una calle grande.

Verticales

1. Vamos al _______ de arte.
2. El actor está en el ______.
3. La ______ de México es grande.
4. Voy a la _____ porque necesito ropa nueva.
6. Los carros van por la _____.

Nombre: ______________________ Fecha: ____________

2 En el Distrito Federal

Imagine you took the following photographs during a trip to Mexico City. Identify what is shown in each photograph.

MODELO:

Es un museo.

1. 

____

____

2. 

____

____

3. 

____

____

4. 

____

____

5. 

____

____

6. 

____

____

Nombre: ______________________________ Fecha: ______________

3 ¿Adónde van a ir?

Look at the map of the center of Mexico City. Write complete sentences, telling where each person is going to go.

MODELO: Yo voy a ir al Zócalo.

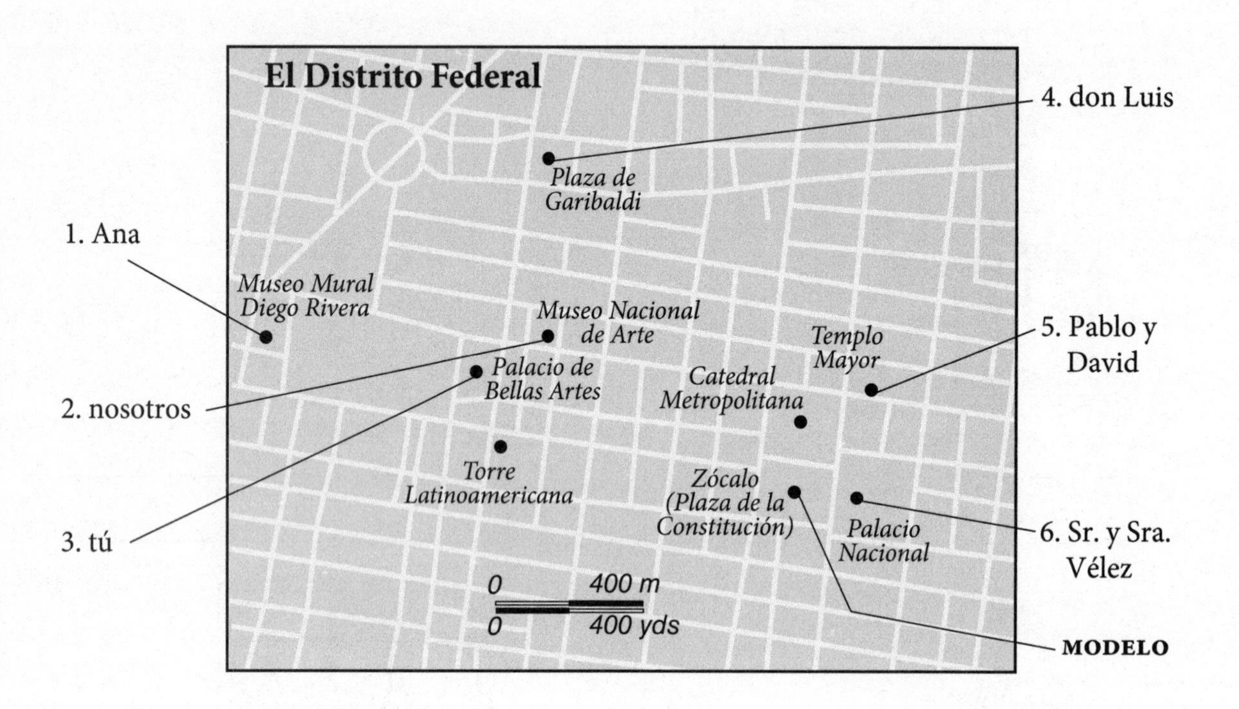

1. ______________________________
2. ______________________________
3. ______________________________
4. ______________________________
5. ______________________________
6. ______________________________

Nombre: ______________________________ Fecha: ______________

4 ¿Qué van a hacer?

Look at the illustrations and write complete sentences, telling what the people are going to do. Use the construction *ir + a* and the verbs from the list.

estudiar   tomar   necesitar   hablar   ir   caminar

MODELO: Ángela
Ángela va a ir al museo.

1. Rafael

____

____

4. nosotros

____

____

2. los señores

____

____

5. Gustavo

____

____

3. Diana

____

____

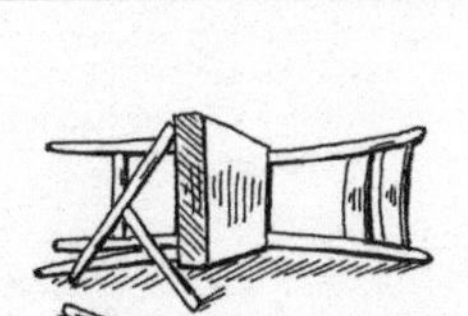

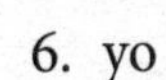

6. yo

____

____

Nombre: ______________________ Fecha: ____________

5 Las tres culturas

Sort the following landmarks and cuisine styles as belonging to a specific historic period of Mexico: pre-Hispanic, colonial, modern. Write them in the table.

Edificios y monumentos
iglesia de Santiago de Tlatelolco
monumento dedicado a los estudiantes
ruinas de templos y pirámides aztecas

Cocina
variada y con influencia global
con insectos como fuente de proteína
con influencia de sabores españoles

Período prehispánico	Período colonial	Tiempos modernos

Now write three sentences about the landmarks and/or cuisine styles of Mexico in different historic periods. Use the model as a guide.

MODELO: La iglesia de Santiago de Tlatelolco es del período colonial.

1. ______________________
2. ______________________
3. ______________________

Nombre: ______________________________ Fecha: ______________

6 En el restaurante

Complete the following conversation that takes place at a restaurant with the appropriate words from the box.

agua	para	menú	ensalada	comer	momento
tomar	cómo	acuerdo	jugo	veo	siempre

MESERO: Buenas tardes, señoritas. ¿Qué van a (1)__________________?

JULIA: Hoy voy a tomar un (2)__________________ de naranja.

CARMEN: Yo quiero un (3)__________________ mineral.

MESERO: ¡(4)__________________ no! ¿Y (5)__________________ comer?

JULIA: Pues, quiero pescado pero no (6)__________________ pescado en el (7)__________________... ¡Aquí está! Yo quiero pescado con una (8)__________________.

MESERO: ¿Y Ud., señorita?

CARMEN: (9)__________________ como pollo pero hoy voy a (10)__________________ pescado.

MESERO: De (11)__________________. Un (12)__________________, por favor.

Nombre: ______________________________ Fecha: ______________

7 Completa el menú

Imagine you work at Restaurante Los Amigos. Complete the menu by writing the items in the box under the appropriate headings.

naranja refresco ensalada de tomate pollo frijoles

Restaurante Los Amigos

ENSALADAS

(1)______________________ $3.50
Ensalada mixta $4.50

PLATOS TÍPICOS
Quesadillas.......... $5.00
Tacos mixtos.......... $6.25

(2)______________ en mole.......... $7.50
Enchiladas verdes.......... $6.75

PLATOS VEGETARIANOS

(3)______________ negros.......... $4.50
Burritos vegeterianos.......... $5.50

BEBIDAS

Jugo de (4)______________ $1.25

(5)______________ $1.25
Agua mineral $1.25

8 ¿Quién comprende?

Tell who understands by completing each sentence with the present tense of *comprender.*

1. Nuria y yo______________
2. Los estudiantes ______________
3. La profesora Díaz ______________
4. Tú ______________
5. Yo ______________
6. Vosotros ______________

Nombre: ______________________ Fecha: ______________

9 ¿Qué comen?

Write a sentence telling what each person eats.

MODELO: Paco 

Paco come pizza.

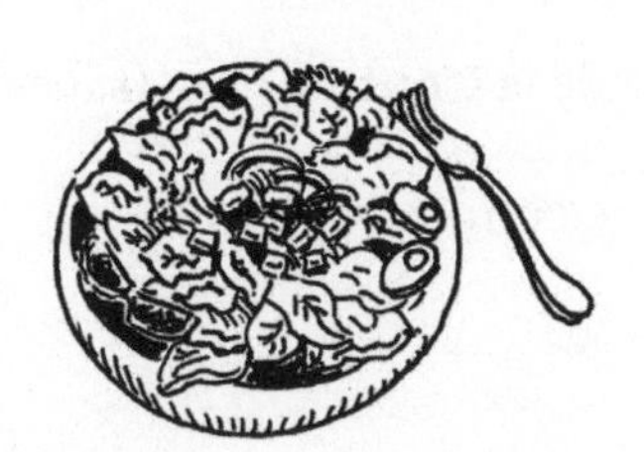

1. yo

____

____

2. Uds.

____

____

3. Alicia

____

____

4. tú

____

____

5. nosotros

____

____

Nombre: ______________________________ Fecha: ______________

10 ¿Qué hacen?

What is everyone doing downtown? Complete the sentences with the present tense of the verbs in parentheses.

1. Carlos y Elvira ____________________ en el Restaurante Delicias. (comer)
2. Yo ____________________ el arte de Frida Kahlo en un museo. (ver)
3. Humberto ____________________ el periódico en la Plaza San Juan. (leer)
4. El médico le ____________________ una pregunta al señor Durán. (hacer)
5. Tú no ____________________ dónde está la Plaza de la Constitución. (saber)
6. Nosotros ____________________ muchos museos y teatros. (ver)
7. Cristina y José ____________________ en el metro. (leer)
8. Yo ____________________ una gira (*tour*) por el centro. (hacer)

11 Una carta de Armando

Complete Armando's letter with the correct forms of the verbs *saber*, *comer*, *ver*, *ir*, *comprender* and *hacer*.

¡Hola Graciela!

¿(1)____________________ tú que Juan y yo estamos en el Distrito Federal? ¡Es una ciudad fantástica! Al mediodía nosotros siempre (2)____________________ mole poblano y por las tardes (3)____________________ mucho arte en los museos. Mañana, yo (4)____________________ a ver a Óscar. Él (5)____________________ y habla inglés. ¿Y tú? ¿Cómo estás? ¿Qué (6)____________________ en San Antonio? ¿(7)____________________ tacos? Yo (8)____________________ muchas preguntas, ¿verdad?

Bueno, hasta pronto.

Tu amigo,
Armando

Nombre: ______________________________ Fecha: ______________

12 ¿Verdad?

Combine elements from each column to write six complete, logical questions with the tag word *verdad.*

MODELO: Conchita va al colegio, ¿verdad?

Conchita	hacer	una revista
mis amigos	comer	muchas preguntas
yo	ver	inglés y español
tú y Mario	saber	pescado
nosotros	comprender	al colegio
Francisca	leer	el edificio grande
vosotros	ir	mi número de teléfono

1. ______________________________

2. ______________________________

3. ______________________________

4. ______________________________

5. ______________________________

6. ______________________________

Nombre: ______________________________ Fecha: ______________

Unidad 4

Lección A

1 La familia Muñoz

Complete the following sentences about the Muñoz family, using the family tree as a reference.

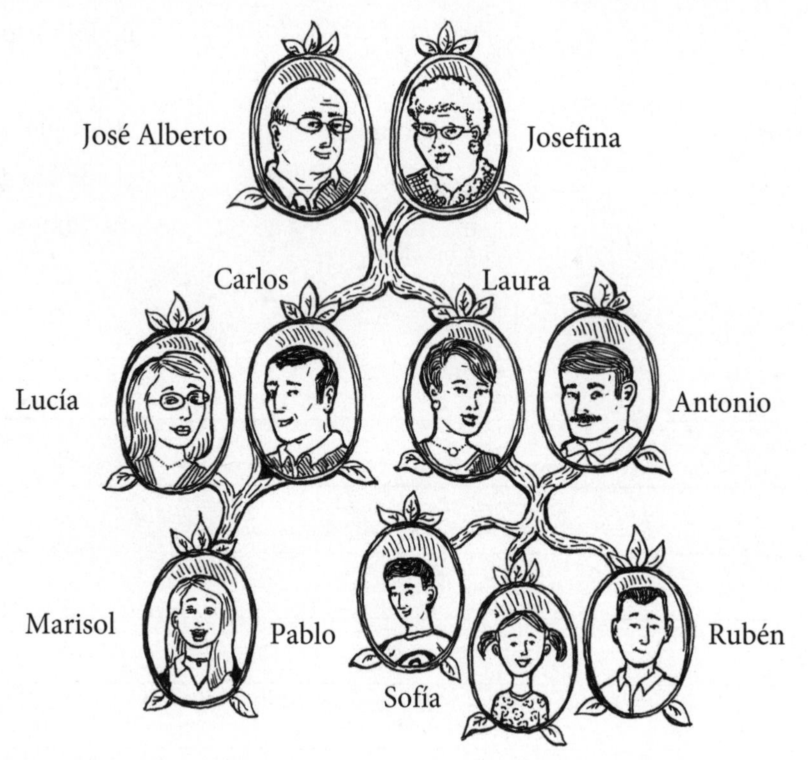

1. Marisol es la ______________________ única de Carlos y Lucía.
2. Los ______________________ de Marisol son José Alberto y Josefina.
3. José Alberto y Josefina tienen dos ______________________ y cuatro ______________________.
4. Laura, la ______________________ de Carlos, es la ______________________ de Marisol.
5. Pablo, Sofía y Rubén son los ______________________ de Carlos y los ______________________ de Marisol.
6. La ______________________ de Carlos es Lucía. Ella es la ______________________ de Marisol.

Nombre: ______________________ Fecha: ______________

2 Crucigrama

Complete the following crossword puzzle with words you learned in the lesson.

Horizontales

3. El ____ de mi primo es mi tío.
5. El padre de mi padre es mi ____.
6. La familia vive en una ____.
7. El hermano de mi madre es mi ____.
9. El hijo de mi hermana es mi ____.
10. Estamos en Puerto Rico pero ____ en Nueva York.

Verticales

1. El hijo de mis padres es mi ____.
2. Abuelos, tíos, primos son ____.
3. El sobrino de mi madre es mi ____.
4. Mi abuelo es el ____ de mi abuela.
8. Él es hijo ____ porque no tiene hermanos.

Nombre: ______________________________ Fecha: ______________

3 Mis primos de Ponce

Rewrite the following sentences, replacing the underlined words with the words in parentheses. Make any necessary changes to the form of the verbs and the adjectives.

MODELO: Mi tía es muy simpática. (mis abuelos)
Mis abuelos son muy simpáticos.

1. Mi tío favorito vive en Ponce, Puerto Rico. (mis primos)

____

2. El museo de arte de Ponce es fantástico. (las playas)

____

3. Hay un restaurante nuevo muy bueno. (una tienda)

____

4. Todos los amigos de mi primo Raúl son divertidos. (las hermanas)

____

5. Mi prima es guapa y popular. (mis primos)

____

6. La casa de mis tíos es grande y bonita. (el carro)

____

Nombre: ____________________ Fecha: __________

4 Fotos de la familia

Your cousin found an old family album and is wondering who is who in the photographs. Answer her questions in the affirmative, using appropriate possessive adjectives.

MODELO: ¿Es ella mi tía?
Sí, es tu tía.

1. ¿Es ella la abuela de nosotros?

____

2. ¿Son los hermanos de Ernesto?

____

3. ¿Es el señor el padre de Carolina?

____

4. ¿Son mis primos?

____

5. ¿Es la señora guapa tu madre?

____

6. ¿Es él mi sobrino?

____

7. ¿Es el muchacho el primo de nosotros?

____

8. ¿Es ella la esposa de tío Manolo?

____

9. ¿Son ellos tus hermanos?

____

10. ¿Los señores son los padres de tu madre?

____

Nombre: ______________________________ Fecha: ______________

5 Las fotos de José

Help José write labels for the photographs he is putting up on his personal website. Complete each phrase with the appropriate possessive adjective.

MODELO: Pedro y su hermana

1. Carmen y ______________ amigas
2. yo y ______________ abuelo
3. don Tomás y ______________ hijos
4. mi amigo y ______________ parientes
5. nosotros y ______________ profesor
6. el Sr. y la Sra. Ramos y ______________ sobrina
7. yo y ______________ primos
8. doña Julia y ______________ esposo

6 Mi familia vive en Puerto Rico

Complete the following sentences with the present tense of the verb *vivir*.

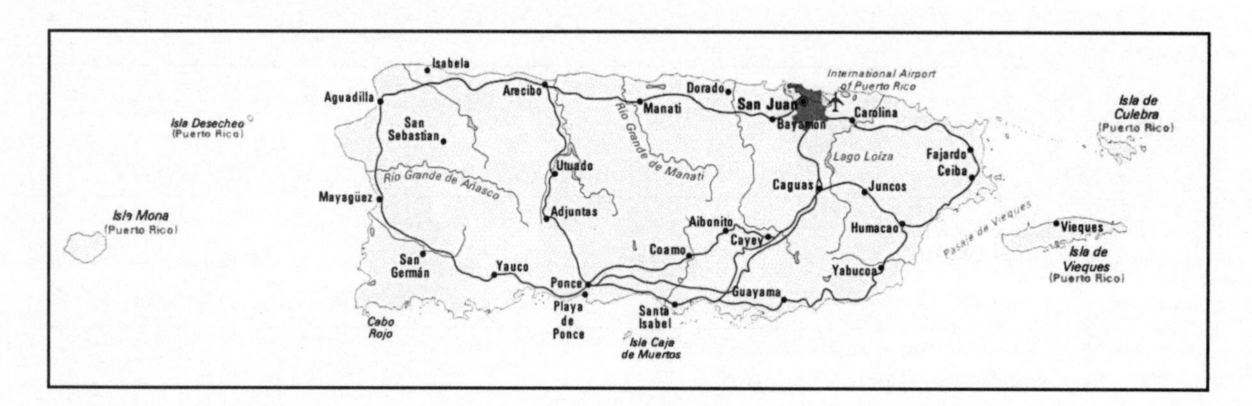

1. Nosotros ________________ en Puerto Rico.
2. Mis abuelos ________________ en Arecibo.
3. Mi hermano Hernán ________________ en Mayagüez.
4. Yo ________________ en San Juan con mis padres.
5. Mi prima Paulina ________________ en Ponce.
6. Mis tíos ________________ en Fajardo.
7. ¿Y tú? ¿Dónde ________________?

Nombre: ______________________________ Fecha: ______________

7 ¡Voy a Puerto Rico!

Enrique is writing an e-mail to a friend. Complete his message with the present tense of the verbs *vivir*, *ir* and *salir*.

CORREO | Nuevo | Enviar | Insertar | Responder | Enrique

Entrada
Spam (1)
Borradores
Eliminados
Contactos
Notas
Archivar
Grupos

De: Enrique

Para: Jorge

Asunto: ¡Hola!

¡Hola!

Estoy en la clase de computación. (1)______________ a las dos de la tarde. ¿A qué hora (2)______________ tú? ¿Sabes? Mañana yo (3)______________ a ir con mi madre a Puerto Rico. En Puerto Rico (4)______________ mis abuelos. Ellos (5)______________ muy cerca de la playa. Nosotros (6)______________ en avión porque (7)______________ en Nueva York y Puerto Rico está lejos. El avión (8)______________ a las diez de la mañana. Mi hermano no (9)______________ porque él estudia en España. Él (10)______________ en Barcelona con un primo de mi padre. Ellos siempre están en casa; no (11)______________ de Barcelona. ¿Y tú, Jorge? ¿(12)______________ a ir a otra ciudad en el verano?

Enrique

Nombre: ______________________________ Fecha: ______________

8 Los idiomas de Puerto Rico

Read the following statements about Puerto Rico and decide whether they are *cierto* (true) or *falso* (false). Write **C** or **F** in the space provided.

______ 1. There are two official languages in Puerto Rico.

______ 2. *Huracán* is an African word.

______ 3. Spanish was the only language in Puerto Rico until 1950.

______ 4. The African word *mondongo* means "tripe soup."

______ 5. Fifty-one percent of Puerto Ricans do not want English to be the only language in the country.

______ 6. If a Puerto Rican invites you to *lonchar*, he or she is inviting you to have lunch.

9 Puerto Rico

How well do you know Puerto Rico? Match the name of the places on the left with the appropriate description in English on the right.

______ 1. el Yunque

______ 2. el castillo de San Felipe del Morro

______ 3. la isla del encanto

______ 4. San Juan

______ 5. Luquillo

A. Puerto Rico's nickname

B. Puerto Rico's capital

C. a beautiful beach

D. a tropical rain forest

E. a fort built in 1591 to protect the island

Nombre: ______________________________ Fecha: ______________

10 ¿Cómo está?

Match the situation in English on the left with the appropriate expression in Spanish on the right. Write the letter of your choice in the space provided.

______	1. Your brother is going to his first job interview.	A. Está triste.
______	2. Sergio's dog just died.	B. Está contento.
______	3. Víctor is wearing a bathing suit to snowboard.	C. Está nervioso.
______	4. Miguel got an A+ on his exam.	D. Está cansado.
______	5. Your uncle worked two night shifts.	E. Está enfermo.
______	6. Your grandfather has the flu.	F. Está loco.

11 No es verdad

Rewrite each of the following sentences, replacing the underlined word with its opposite.

MODELO: Hilda está <u>mal.</u>
Hilda está bien.

1. Nuestra casa está limpia.

____

2. El museo está cerrado hoy.

____

3. Humberto está muy contento.

____

4. Juanita está enferma.

____

5. El jugo de naranja está frío.

____

6. La mesa cerca de la ventana está ocupada.

____

Nombre: ______________________ Fecha: ____________

12 ¿Cómo están?

Complete the following descriptions with the correct form of *estar* and an appropriate adjective.

MODELO: 

El pollo está caliente.

1. 

El parque ______________________

______________________.

2. 

Los chicos ______________________

______________________.

3. 

La chica ______________________

______________________.

4. 

Tu ______________________

______________________.

5. 

Las ventanas ______________________

______________________.

6. 

El estudiante ______________________

______________________.

7. 

Mis tíos ______________________

______________________.

8. 

Nosotros ______________________

______________________.

Nombre: ______________________ Fecha: __________

13 En la red social

Imagine you are on social media talking about your family, real or imaginary. Write six to eight sentences describing your family. Include their names and relationships, where they live, and how they are.

Nombre: ______________________ Fecha: ______________

Lección B

1 Mis nuevos amigos

Imagine you are an exchange student in the Dominican Republic and you write a letter to your parents at home. Complete the letter with the words from the list.

hacer	bailar	escuchar	jugar	gustar
patinar	nadar	tocar	partido	ver

Hola, mamá y papá:

¿Cómo están? Yo estoy bien. Me (1)______________ *mucho estudiar en la República Dominicana. Es un país fantástico.*

Tengo dos nuevos amigos. Se llaman Rafael y Érica. Son muy simpáticos. A Rafael le gusta (2)______________ *al béisbol y* (3)______________ *el piano. A Érica le gusta* (4)______________ *sobre ruedas y* (5)______________ *salsa y merengue. A los dos les gusta* (6)______________ *la radio pero no les gusta* (7)______________ *la televisión. Mañana nosotros vamos a* (8)______________ *en la playa. Y en la tarde, vamos a ir a un* (9)______________ *de béisbol. ¡Qué divertido!*

Bueno, hasta luego. Voy a (10)______________ *la tarea.*

Los quiero,

Ricardo

Nombre: ______________________ Fecha: __________

2 ¿Qué te gusta hacer?

Look at each illustration and say whether or not you like doing the activity pictured.

MODELO: 

Me gusta tocar el piano./No me gusta tocar el piano.

1. 

____

____

2.

____

____

3.

____

____

4.

____

____

5. 

____

____

6. 

____

____

7. 

____

____

8. 

____

____

Nombre: ______________________________ Fecha: ______________

3 Nos gusta mucho

You and your friends are listing all the things and activities you like about the Dominican Republic. Complete each sentence with either *nos gusta* or *nos gustan.*

1. ______________________ las playas bonitas.
2. ______________________ los partidos de béisbol.
3. ______________________ el merengue.
4. ______________________ los edificios en Santo Domingo.
5. ______________________ ir de compras.
6. ______________________ el Museo de Arte Moderno.
7. ______________________ los parques ecológicos.
8. ______________________ nadar en Boca Chica.

Nombre: ______________________ Fecha: __________

4 ¿Qué les gusta?

Write complete sentences, saying what the following people like to do.

MODELO: Selena / contestar en clase
A Selena le gusta contestar en clase.

1. Juan Pablo / jugar al béisbol

____

2. tus amigos / ver televisión

____

3. nosotros / las ensaladas

____

4. tú / los conciertos de rock

____

5. la abuela / leer revistas

____

6. profesor Bolaños / hacer preguntas

____

7. yo / los chicos inteligentes

____

8. mis hermanos / ir en tren

____

Nombre: ______________________________ Fecha: ______________

5 Conexión dominicana

Read the following profiles of teenagers in the Dominican Republic who are looking for pen pals. Then answer the questions.

Nombre: María Luz Guerra
Dirección: mlguerra@cable.com
Edad: 15 años
Pasatiempos: bailar, ir al cine, jugar al béisbol

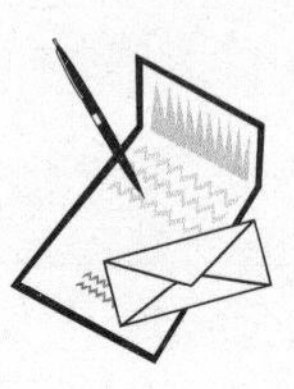

Nombre: Rodrigo Vargas
Dirección: vargas2@inter.net
Edad: 16 años
Pasatiempos: tocar el piano, leer, escuchar la radio

Nombre: Juan Luis Alarcón
Dirección: alarcon111@red.dr
Edad: 17 años
Pasatiempos: ir a la playa, salir con amigos, cantar

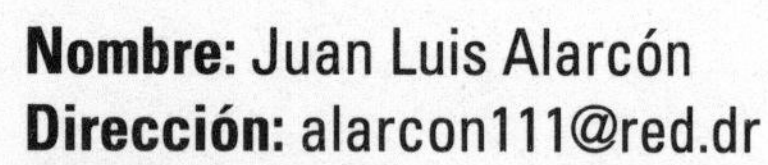

Nombre: Elena Jiménez
Dirección: elenaj@cable.com
Edad: 15 años
Pasatiempos: leer, escuchar la radio, patinar sobre ruedas

Nombre: Antonio J. Díaz
Dirección: adiaz@latino.net
Edad: 16 años
Pasatiempos: jugar al béisbol, leer, nadar, ir al cine

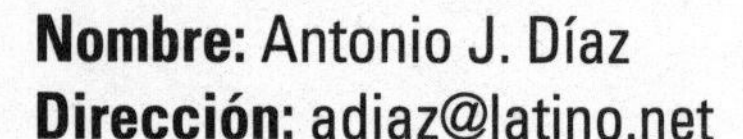

Nombre: Consuelo Valero
Dirección: conval@inter.net
Edad: 17 años
Pasatiempos: salir con amigos, ir al cine, bailar

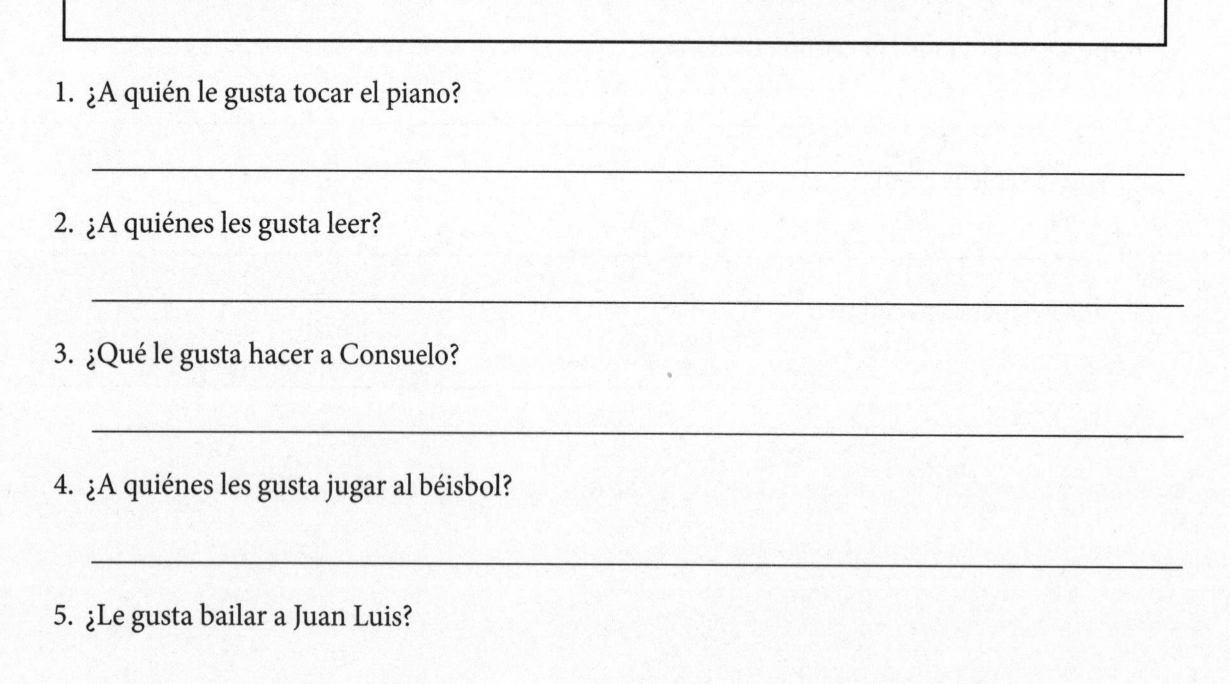

1. ¿A quién le gusta tocar el piano?

   ____

2. ¿A quiénes les gusta leer?

   ____

3. ¿Qué le gusta hacer a Consuelo?

   ____

4. ¿A quiénes les gusta jugar al béisbol?

   ____

5. ¿Le gusta bailar a Juan Luis?

   ____

6. ¿A ti qué te gusta hacer?

   ____

Nombre: ____ Fecha: ________________

6 La familia dominicana

Read the following statements about Dominican families and decide whether they are *cierto* (true) or *falso* (false). Write **C** or **F** in the space provided.

______ 1. The traditional Hispanic family includes parents, children, grandparents, aunts, and uncles.

______ 2. Today the average Dominican household consists of eight people.

______ 3. Family members might immigrate to other countries.

______ 4. Parents are opting to have more children than before.

______ 5. Many traditional Dominican values have disappeared.

______ 6. Dominicans have close relationships with their friends and neighbors.

7 La República Dominicana

Based on what you have learned about the Dominican Republic, complete the sentences on the left with the phrases on the right.

______ 1. Uno de los músicos favoritos de los dominicanos es…

______ 2. El merengue es un ritmo…

______ 3. El merengue representa…

______ 4. La güira es de la cultura…

______ 5. Los dominicanos escuchan música…

______ 6. El merengue es un baile…

______ 7. La bachata tiene su origen en…

______ 8. La bachata es un ritmo…

______ 9. La palabra "bachata" tiene su origen en…

______ 10. La guitarra, la güira, el tambor bongó y las maracas son los instrumentos de...

A. en todas partes.

B. romántico.

C. Juan Luis Guerra.

D. divertido.

E. la bachata.

F. una unión de culturas.

G. antiguo.

H. taína.

I. África.

J. los años sesenta

Nombre: ______________________________ Fecha: ______________

8 Juego

Write the opposite words in the spaces provided. Then unscramble the circled letters to complete the sentence on the bottom.

1. rápido ___ ___ (___) ___ ___
2. generosa ___ ___ ___ ___ ___ (___) ___
3. divertido ___ ___ ___ (___) ___ ___ ___ ___
4. tonto ___ ___ ___ (___) ___ ___ ___ ___ ___ (___) ___
5. bonitos ___ ___ ___ (___)
6. alta ___ (___) ___ ___
7. mala ___ ___ (___) ___ ___
8. gordo ___ (___) ___ ___ ___ ___ ___
9. fácil ___ ___ ___ ___ ___ (___) ___
10. rubia ___ ___ ___ ___ (___) ___

La clase de español es ______________________________.

9 ¿Cómo es?

Complete the following descriptions, according to the pictures.

MODELO: es baja.

1. Raquel es ______________________.

4. La clase es ______________________.

2. Don Fernando es ______________________.

5. Quique es ______________________.

3. El avión es ______________________.

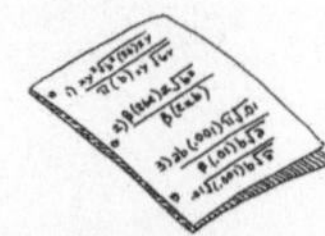

6. La tarea es ______________________.

Nombre: ______________________________ Fecha: ______________

10 ¿Qué quiere decir?

Match the description in English on the left with the correct expression in Spanish on the right.

______	1. The fruit is not ripe.	A. Está guapa.
______	2. Marta looks pretty today.	B. Es en el parque.
______	3. Marta is at the park.	C. Es guapa.
______	4. Marta is pretty.	D. Está verde.
______	5. Marta's backpack is green.	E. Es verde.
______	6. The concert is in the park.	F. Está en el parque.

11 ¿Cuál es el verbo correcto?

Choose the verb that logically completes each sentence.

1. Mi padre (es / está) un señor bueno, inteligente y generoso.
2. Lorenzo va a ir al médico porque (es / está) enfermo.
3. Mis hermanos y yo (somos / estamos) de Nueva York.
4. ¿Dónde (es / está) el concierto de Marc Anthony?
5. ¿Por qué (eres / estás) nerviosa, Lita?
6. La casa de Juan (es / está) cerca de la playa.

Nombre: ______________________________ Fecha: ______________

12 *¿Ser o estar?*

Complete the following conversation with the correct forms of the verbs *ser* or *estar*.

MARTÍN: ¡Hola, Berta! ¿Cómo (1)______________?

BERTA: Bien, gracias. Oye, (2)______________ muy guapo.

MARTÍN: Gracias. Voy a una fiesta.

BERTA: ¿Sí? ¿Dónde (3)______________ la fiesta?

MARTÍN: En la casa de Lorena.

BERTA: ¿Quién (4)__________Lorena?

MARTÍN: Lorena (5)__________ la prima de Carlos. Ella (6)__________ en nuestra clase de computación. (7)______________ de la República Dominicana.

BERTA: (8)________ la chica alta, delgada y morena, ¿verdad?

MARTÍN: Sí. ¿Quieres ir a la fiesta?

BERTA: No, gracias. (9)________ ocupada.

Nombre: ____ Fecha: _______________

13 Hay un concierto

Look at the following advertisement for a concert. Use the information in it to answer the questions.

1. ¿Cuándo es el concierto?

____

2. ¿Dónde es el concierto?

____

3. ¿Quién es el cantante?

____

4. ¿Cómo es él? ¿Moreno o rubio?

____

5. ¿Te gusta ir a conciertos? ¿Por qué?

____

Nombre: ______________________________ Fecha: ______________

Unidad 5

Lección A

1 En la tienda

Complete the following sentences logically with the appropriate words.

lástima	DVD	estéreo	dinero	reproductor
disco	quemador	artículos	caramba	canción

1. Los chicos entran en la tienda de ______________________ electrónicos.
2. Mauricio busca el ______________________ compacto con la nueva ______________________ de Marc Anthony.
3. ¡______________________! La tienda no tiene el CD, solamente *(only)* tiene el ______________________ de su nueva película.
4. Carolina ve un ______________________, un ______________________ de MP3 y un ______________________ de CDs.
5. ¡Qué ______________________! Ella no tiene ______________________ para comprar los artículos electrónicos.

2 ¿Qué tienen?

What do the following people have in their suitcases as they leave on a trip to Costa Rica? Complete the sentences with the present tense of the verb *tener*.

1. Arturo ______________________ un mapa de Costa Rica.
2. Nosotros ______________________ tres discos compactos de música salsa.
3. Irene y Maite ______________________ cinco camisetas.
4. Tú ______________________ un diccionario de español.
5. Yo ______________________ dos libros sobre las selvas tropicales.
6. Don César ______________________ mucho dinero.

Nombre: ____ Fecha: ______________

3 ¡Qué sorpresa!

What a coincidence! Write a sentence saying that the person in parentheses also has it. Be sure to change the verb forms when necessary.

MODELO: Guillermo tiene veinte años. (yo)
Yo también tengo veinte años.

1. El Sr. Camacho tiene un reproductor de MP3. (mis primos)

   ____

2. Yo tengo tres discos compactos de Santana. (Maricela)

   ____

3. La profesora Ruiz tiene un mapa de San José. (nosotros)

   ____

4. Lorena tiene un quemador de CDs. (tú)

   ____

5. Sergio y Mateo tienen un estéreo japonés. (yo)

   ____

6. Mi hermano tiene quince años. (Ramón)

   ____

Nombre: ______________________________ Fecha: ______________

4 En el autobús

Imagine you are in a tour bus in Costa Rica. Look at the drawing and write what everyone is holding.

MODELO: Daniel
Daniel tiene una revista.

1. Olga

____

2. los chicos

____

3. Ángela

____

4. el Sr. López y Ángela

____

5. yo

____

6. tú

____

Nombre: ______________________________ Fecha: ______________

5 ¡Qué país!

While visiting Costa Rica, you are awed by some of its sights. Write an appropriate expression for each situation using *qué* + noun.

MODELO: You see *volcán Irazú* with its enormous crater.
¡Qué volcán!

1. You go to a large store in Sarchí where they sell colorful, hand-painted wooden carts.

____

2. You visit the national theater in San José, a beautiful building decorated in rococo style.

____

3. At Jacó Beach, you run into one of your classmates, who is also visiting Costa Rica.

____

4. You visit Braulio Carrillo, a national park with over 6,000 plant species.

____

5. You watch an interesting movie about Columbus' visit to Puerto Limón.

____

6. You see a city bus colorfully decorated with painted murals and lights.

____

7. You watch an exciting soccer game between Saprissa and Alajuela.

____

8. Tomorrow you go back home. You feel it is a shame that the trip is over.

____

Nombre: ______________________________ Fecha: ______________

6 Un país de gran riqueza

Complete the following sentences about Costa Rica with the appropriate expressions from the list.

environment	hot springs	*pura vida*	volcano	*ticos*
gold and silver	electronics	Arenal	natural parks	

1. Costa Rica may be a small country, but you can do many activities there. For example, you can visit an active ______________________.

2. The name Costa Rica was given by Christopher Columbus. When he disembarked there in 1502, he thought the area had a lot of ______________________.

3. The Costa Ricans are very involved in protecting the ______________________. They want to preserve their natural resources and encourage ecotourism.

4. There are a lot of ______________________ because it's very important to protect the wildlife.

5. The ______________________ volcano is a very popular place to visit for both locals and guests.

6. Also, you can visit the ______________________ and enjoy a moment of relaxation.

7. There are many important industries besides tourism in Costa Rica, such as agriculture, pharmaceuticals, and ______________________.

8. When you go to Costa Rica, you will hear some regional words and expressions. For example, ______________________ means "pure life," and Costa Ricans refer to themselves as ______________________.

Nombre: ____ Fecha: ________________

7 Costa Rica

Read the following statements about Costa Rica and decide whether they are *cierto* (true) or *falso* (false). Write **C** or **F** in the space provided.

_____ 1. Costa Rica is a country with no army.

_____ 2. Costa Rica has never been actively involved in peace processes.

_____ 3. Costa Rica is waging war against ignorance and poverty.

_____ 4. Costa Rica invests little money in education and culture compared to other Latin American countries.

_____ 5. Less than half of the adults in Costa Rica can read and write.

_____ 6. Costa Ricans show their love for their country during the Independence Day celebrations.

Nombre: ______________________________ Fecha: ______________

8 Crucigrama

Complete the following crossword puzzle.

Horizontales

2. No esta semana; la semana que ___.
3. No mucho.
4. Animal que hace miau.
5. Hacer la ___ para ir de viaje.
7. Hay siete días en una ___.
9. Tienda de libros.

Verticales

1. El tenis, el fútbol y el béisbol son ___.
5. ___ en bicicleta.
6. ___ a un amigo por teléfono.
8. La tienda ___ a las 10:00 A.M.

Nombre: ______________________________ Fecha: ______________

9 Identifica

Circle the verb and underline the direct object in each of the following sentences.

Modelo: Todos los días (llevo) el perro al parque.

1. Víctor compra una revista en la librería.
2. El señor Domínguez hace las maletas.
3. Tú siempre escuchas la radio, ¿verdad?
4. Mis compañeros ven la película de Penélope Cruz.
5. La estudiante nueva contesta las preguntas del profesor.
6. Todas las mañanas yo leo el periódico.
7. Mi tío toma el metro cada día.
8. Los ticos comen gallo pinto.
9. Doña Rosita hace un viaje la semana que viene.

10 La *a personal*

Write the *a personal* only in those sentences that require it.

1. Mi padre tiene _____ tres hermanos y una hermana.
2. Yo veo _____ mi tío Antonio cada domingo.
3. Mi tío tiene _____ un gato muy gordo.
4. Mi hermana siempre llama _____ nuestros primos.
5. Ellos escuchan _____ Shakira.
6. Mis amigos y yo leemos _____ revistas cómicas.
7. La semana que viene vamos a ver _____ un partido de tenis.
8. Mi madre lleva _____ mi hermana al médico.

Nombre: ______________________ Fecha: __________

11 ¿Lo ves?

Look at the drawing and answer the questions, using direct object pronouns.

MODELO: ¿Ves el piano?
No, no lo veo.

1. ¿Ves el mapa de Costa Rica? ______________________
2. ¿Ves la computadora? ______________________
3. ¿Ves el reproductor de DVDs? ______________________
4. ¿Ves los libros? ______________________
5. ¿Ves el estéreo? ______________________
6. ¿Ves las ventanas? ______________________
7. ¿Ves la pizarra? ______________________
8. ¿Ves el dinero? ______________________
9. ¿Ves los pupitres? ______________________
10. ¿Me ves? ______________________

Nombre: ______________________ Fecha: ______________

12 Complementos directos

Rewrite the following sentences, changing the direct object nouns to direct object pronous.

MODELO: Graciela lee revistas en español.
Graciela las lee.

1. Javier tiene el reproductor de CDs.

____

2. Verónica ve a los niños.

____

3. No comprendo las palabras.

____

4. Mario llama a la profesora de inglés.

____

5. Nosotros tomamos el tren.

____

13 ¿Quién lo hace?

Answer the following questions, using the cues in parentheses and direct object pronouns.

MODELO: ¿Quién llama a Enrique? (el Sr. Garza)
El Sr. Garza lo llama.

1. ¿Quién compra un reproductor de CDs? (Manuela)

____

2. ¿Quiénes me ven todos los días? (los compañeros)

____

3. ¿Quién tiene el CD de Miguel Bosé? (esta tienda)

____

4. ¿Quién te escucha cantar? (el perro)

____

5. ¿Quiénes toman jugo de tomate? (Alex y María)

____

Nombre: ______________________________ Fecha: ______________

14 La semana que viene

Look at Federico's agenda and answer the following questions. Use direct object pronouns when appropriate.

LUNES 8	**JUEVES 11**
comprar el libro de historia	*llevar al gato a casa de tía Marta*
llamar a Lucía	
MARTES 9	**VIERNES 12**
estudiar para el examen de inglés	*hacer la maleta*
	ver la nueva película
MIÉRCOLES 10	**SÁBADO 13 / DOMINGO 14**
ir a la práctica de béisbol	*tomar el autobús a Guanacaste*

1. ¿Dónde crees *(you think)* que Federico compra el libro de historia?

   ____

2. ¿Tiene Federico la práctica de béisbol el martes?

   ____

3. ¿Adónde lleva al gato el jueves?

   ____

4. ¿Cuándo va a estudiar inglés?

   ____

5. ¿Adónde toma el autobús Federico?

   ____

6. ¿Cuándo hace la maleta?

   ____

7. ¿Qué día llama Federico a Lucía?

   ____

8. ¿Dónde crees *(you think)* que Federico ve la película el viernes?

   ____

Nombre: ______________________________ Fecha: ______________

Lección B

1 Diciembre

Complete the sentences based on the following calendar.

DICIEMBRE						
LUNES	MARTES	MIÉRCOLES	JUEVES	VIERNES	SÁBADO	DOMINGO
	1	2	3	4	5	6
7	8	9	10	11	12	13
14	15	16	17	18	19	20
21	22	23	24	25	26	27
28	29	30	31			

1. Hoy es miércoles 9. (Ayer / Mañana) fue martes 8.
2. Hoy es el 31 de diciembre. Mañana es el (primero de enero / 30 de diciembre).
3. Hoy es el 17 de diciembre. Anteayer fue el (15 / 16) de diciembre.
4. Hoy es el veinticinco de diciembre. Es (Nochevieja / Navidad).
5. Mañana es el 11 de diciembre. Hoy es (jueves / viernes).
6. Hoy es lunes 21. Pasado mañana es (miércoles 23 / jueves 24).
7. Hoy es el 29 de diciembre. (Anteayer / Ayer) fue el 27 de diciembre.
8. Mañana es Noche Vieja. Hoy es el (24 / 30) de diciembre.

Nombre: ______________________________ Fecha: ______________

2 Un cumpleaños especial

Complete the following paragraph with the words from the list.

mayor	mucho	fue	viene	veintitrés
cumpleaños	temprano	fantástico	nueve	celebrarlo

Ayer, (1)______________________ de noviembre, (2)______________________

mi (3)______________________. Para (4)______________________, mis amigos

y yo fuimos al concierto de Ricardo Montaner. Todos los años Ricardo Montaner

(5)______________________ a nuestra ciudad. Me gustan

(6)______________________ sus canciones. Mi hermana

(7)______________________ de 19 años también fue al concierto. Fue a las

(8)______________________ de la noche pero llegamos al Estadio Nacional

(9)______________________, a las siete y media. ¡Fue (10)______________________!

Nombre: ______________________ Fecha: ____________

3 ¿De dónde vienen?

Everyone in the tour group visited a different place in Nicaragua. Complete the following sentences with the present tense of *venir* to find out where everyone comes from.

MODELO: Los señores Castro vienen de Rivas.

1. Yo ______________________ de Granada.
2. Samuel ______________________ de León.
3. Flor y Laura ______________________ de Managua.
4. Tú ______________________ de Masaya.
5. El Sr. Quiroga ______________________ de Bluefields.
6. Los compañeros de Tobías ______________________ de Matagalpa.

4 ¿Cuándo vienen?

When is everyone coming? Use the clues given and the present tense of *venir* to write complete sentences.

MODELO: José / mañana
José viene mañana.

1. Mateo y Mauricio / pasado mañana

   ____

2. tú / la semana que viene

   ____

3. nosotros / el primero de enero

   ____

4. Hortensia / hoy

   ____

5. mis parientes / el fin de semana

   ____

Nombre: ______________________________ Fecha: ______________

5 ¿Cómo vienen a la fiesta?

Look at the illustrations and write complete sentences, telling how everyone is arriving to the party.

Modelo: Alber

Alberto viene en moto.

1. Raúl 

____

____

5. tú 

____

____

2. Sara y Rosa 

____

____

6. Doña Julia 

____

____

3. Dolores 

____

____

7. mis primos 

____

____

4. nosotros 

____

____

8. yo 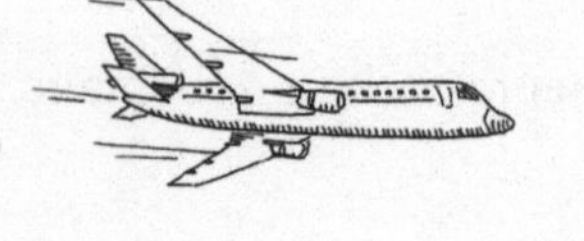

____

____

Nombre: ______________________________ Fecha: ______________

6 Los días de fiesta en Nicaragua

The following web page about Nicaragua has some words missing. Complete the paragraph with the words and expressions from the list.

tradicionales procesión Managua patronales festivo Minguito

caballos y carrozas católica agosto Santo Domingo

En Nicaragua las principales fiestas están relacionadas con la religión

(1) ______________________. Muchas ciudades de Nicaragua tienen fiestas

(2) ______________________ en honor a sus santos. Una de las fiestas más

importantes se celebra en la capital del país, (3) ______________________, el

primero y el 10 de (4) ______________________ de cada año. Son las fiestas de

(5) ______________________. Miles de personas salen a las calles y participan

en la (6) ______________________. Una estatua pequeña de Santo Domingo,

llamado también (7) ______________________, es llevada al centro de la

ciudad. El ambiente es (8) ______________________, pues hay música y danzas.

Los espectadores comparten (*share*) comidas y bebidas

(9) ______________________ por el camino. También hay explosiones de

pólvora y un desfile de (10) ______________________.

Nombre: ______________________________ Fecha: ______________

7 Más fiestas nicaragüenses

Based on what you have learned about Nicaragua, match the description on the left with the corresponding holiday on the right.

______ 1. Es el primero y el 10 de agosto.		A. Santo Domingo
______ 2. Se celebra con una procesión de perros.		B. San Lázaro
______ 3. Es el santo patrón de Managua.		C. la Purísima
______ 4. Es la fiesta de la Inmaculada Concepción de la Virgen María.		
______ 5. Es antes de Semana Santa, en la ciudad de Masaya.		
______ 6. Combina la devoción religiosa con el amor hacia los animales.		
______ 7. Es el 8 de diciembre.		

Nombre: ______________________________ Fecha: ______________

8 Doce meses

In the word-square below, find and circle the Spanish names for the twelve months of the year. The words may read horizontally, vertically or diagonally.

A	O	C	T	U	B	R	E	F	E	R
B	C	T	D	Q	U	I	S	E	F	N
R	D	A	S	J	D	G	E	B	H	O
I	K	I	L	U	U	M	P	R	V	V
L	C	V	C	N	E	L	T	E	O	I
M	A	Y	O	I	Q	U	I	R	P	E
A	P	G	L	O	E	L	E	O	L	M
R	W	E	O	R	T	M	M	I	B	B
Z	A	S	D	S	F	G	B	H	T	R
O	K	L	P	X	T	W	R	R	S	E
R	H	E	N	E	R	O	E	J	E	D

9 ¿Cuánto es?

Read the following numbers and write them out, using numerals.

MODELO: mil setecientos 1.700

1. trescientos veinticinco ___________
2. cien mil novecientos dos ___________
3. mil cuatrocientos cincuenta ___________
4. cinco mil ciento veintidós ___________
5. doscientos cuarenta mil ochocientos once ___________
6. novecientos noventa mil quinientos uno ___________
7. setecientos mil cuatrocientos quince ___________
8. cien mil ciento trece ___________

Nombre: ______________________ Fecha: ____________

10 Contesta

Answer the following questions.

1. ¿Cuál es la fecha de hoy?

____

2. ¿Cuándo es el cumpleaños de tu mejor amigo(a)?

____

3. ¿Cuántos años cumple tu amigo(a)? ¿Es joven o viejo?

____

4. ¿En qué fecha es el Día de Año Nuevo?

____

5. ¿Qué año va a ser? ¿Te gusta la idea de estar en ese año?

____

6. ¿Pasan los años rápidamente?

____

Nombre: ______________________ Fecha: ____________

11 ¿Cuánto cuesta?

Look at the following newspaper ad for electronics. Then answer the questions, spelling out the numbers.

MODELO: ¿Cuánto cuesta el microcomponente?
Cuesta ciento cuarenta y nueve mil novecientos.

1. ¿Cuánto cuesta el reproductor DVDs?

____

____

____

2. ¿Cuánto cuesta el video grabador?

____

____

____

3. ¿Cuánto cuesta el equipo Sony MHC-RG22?

____

____

____

4. ¿Cuánto cuesta el equipo Sony MHC-RG33?

____

____

____

Microcomponente SONY CMT-M70, reproductor de CD, 20 W RMSx2, modos DSGx2, sintonizador digital con memoria para 30 emisoras (20 FM/10AM), Deck full logic, control remoto
Cod. 1804130
Antes $179.900 Ahora $149.900

Equipo Sony MHC-RG22. 1300W PMPO, cambiador de 3 CD, Game Sync, ecualizador directo de audio/video, parlante de 3 vías
Cod. 1805446
$ 149.900

Video grabador modelo SLV-LX 77, VHS 6 cabezales Hi-Fi, stereo con sintonizador MTS máxima resolución, búsqueda de programas con perilla, sistema TRILOGIC, cabezales de 19 micrones
cod 1802046
$ 99.900

Reproductor DVD modelo DVP-NS315, Virtual Surround Sonidos envolventes utilizando sólo altavoces de TV, reproduce CD-R/RW/Lectura MP3, reductor de ruidos en líneas verticales.
Cod. 1803091
Antes $ 149.900 Ahora $129.900

Equipo Sony MHC-RG33. 1700W PMPO, cambiador de 3 CD, gabinete hexagonal, Game Sync. ecualizador directo de audio/video, parlante de 3 vías
Cod. 1805442
Antes $ 189.900 Ahora $ 169.900

Nombre: ______________________ Fecha: __________

12 Fechas históricas

Spell out the dates of the following historical dates in Latin American history.

MODELO: Nicaragua declara la independencia de España: 15/9/1821
el quince de septiembre de mil ochocientos veintiuno

1. Cristóbal Colón llega a Cuba: 27/10/1492

2. Hernán Cortés toma la capital de los aztecas: 13/08/1521

3. México declara la independencia de España: 16/09/1810

4. La Universidad de San Marcos en Perú abre: 12/05/1551

5. El huracán Mitch llega a Centroamérica: 31/10/1998

6. Gabriel García Márquez recibe el Premio Nóbel de Literatura: 08/12/1982

7. Crean la Organización de Estados Americanos: 30/04/1948

8. El astronauta costarricense Franklin Chang-Díaz va al espacio: 12/01/1986

Nombre: ______________________________ Fecha: ______________

13 Mi cumpleaños

Write a paragraph in which you say when your birthday is, how old you will be, and whether you like the idea of turning that age a lot or not even a little bit. Also mention who is coming to your birthday and describe your plans for that day.

Nombre: ______________________ Fecha: ____________

Unidad 6

Lección A

1 Crucigrama

Complete the following crossword puzzle with items found in the kitchen and on the dinner table.

Horizontales

1. Pones la ___ antes de comer.
5. Necesitas un ___ para tomar jugo.
6. Los refrescos fríos están en el ____.
7. La ___ da luz artificial.
9. Necesitas una ___ para hacer arepas calientes.

Verticales

2. Necesitas una ___ para limpiarte la boca *(mouth)*.
3. Comes en el ___.
4. Enciendes las ___ para ver de noche.
8. Necesitas un ___ para comer pescado.

Nombre: ______________________ Fecha: ______________

2 Un mensaje en el refrigerador

Sra. Delgado left her sons a message on the refrigerator door. Complete the note, using the appropriate verbs from the list below.

ayudar	cerrar	deben	empezar
encender	pensar	poner	viajar

Hijos:

Tengo que (1)__________ *mañana a Colombia.*

Deben (2)__________ *a su padre a hacer las siguientes cosas:*

Para (3)__________, *deben* (4)__________ *la mesa. Después,* (5)__________ *estudiar.*

Cuando es de noche, tienen que (6)__________ *las ventanas y* (7)__________ *las luces.*

También deben (8)__________ *en el perro y darle de comer.*

Los quiero,

Mamá

Nombre: ______________________________ Fecha: ______________

3 ¿*Deber* o *tener que*?

Complete the following sentences with the correct form of *deber* or *tener que,* whichever is more appropriate.

1. Ramón ____________________ comprar más servilletas de papel.
2. Beatriz y yo ____________________ ayudar en la cocina.
3. Tú ____________________ hacer la tarea de español.
4. Yo ____________________ ir a Caracas el doce de marzo.
5. Uds. no ____________________ ver mucha televisión.
6. Félix ____________________ poner la mesa del comedor.
7. Nosotros no ____________________ lavar los platos hoy.
8. Los estudiantes ____________________ ser más amables con el profesor.

4 *Pensar, pensar de* y *pensar en*

Choose from the different uses of *pensar* to complete each sentence.

MODELO: ¿C tu familia?

A. piensas B. piensas de C. piensas en

1. ¿Qué _____ mi nuevo amigo?
2. ¿Adónde _____ ir de vacaciones?
3. ¿_____ visitar a tus parientes en Colombia?
4. ¿_____ tus abuelos?
5. ¿Qué _____ la idea de ir al cine?
6. ¿Qué _____ hacer el fin de semana?

Nombre: ______________________________ Fecha: ______________

5 ¿En qué piensas?

Complete the following conversation with the appropriate forms of the verb *pensar*.

CLAUDIA: Hola, Alonso. ¿En qué (1)__________________?

ALONSO: (2)__________________ en mi viaje a Venezuela.

CLAUDIA: ¡Qué divertido! Mis padres y yo también (3)__________________ ir a Venezuela.

ALONSO: ¿(4)__________________ Uds. ir a la playa?

CLAUDIA: ¡Claro! Nosotros (5)__________________ ir a Playa Colorada. ¿Y tú?

ALONSO: Yo (6)__________________ ir a Isla Margarita.

CLAUDIA: ¿Cuándo (7)__________________ ir?

ALONSO: (8)__________________ hacer el viaje la próxima semana.

CLAUDIA: ¿Qué (9)__________________ el profesor de tu viaje?

ALONSO: Él (10)__________________ que debo estudiar en la playa.

CLAUDIA: ¡Yo (11)__________________ que es imposible!

6 ¿Qué hacen?

Complete the sentences with the correct forms of the verbs shown in parentheses.

1. Carmen, ¿__________________ ir al concierto de piano con nosotros? (querer)
2. Ella lo __________________ mucho, pero tiene que estudiar. (sentir)
3. Nosotros __________________ comer hallacas en el restaurante venezolano. (pensar)
4. El restaurante __________________ a las diez de la noche. (cerrar)
5. Todas las noches, Marcos y Ana __________________ la televisión. (encender)
6. Yo __________________ leer un buen libro. (preferir)
7. Los chicos __________________ ir al cine. (querer)
8. La película __________________ a las ocho de la noche. (empezar)

Nombre: ______________________________ Fecha: ______________

7 ¿Qué hacen?

Combine words from each column to write six complete, logical sentences. Make sure you use the appropriate forms of the verbs.

mis amigos	cerrar	a estudiar a las siete
yo	empezar	no poder ir a tu fiesta
mi primo	encender	la puerta del refrigerador
tú	preferir	escuchar música
mi familia y yo	querer	mirar una película
los estudiantes	sentir	la radio del carro

1. ______________________________
2. ______________________________
3. ______________________________
4. ______________________________
5. ______________________________
6. ______________________________

8 Venezuela

Read the following statements and decide whether they are *cierto* (true) or *falso* (false). Write **C** or **F** in the space provided.

______ 1. Venezuela is a mix of European, indigenous, and African cultures.

______ 2. Maracaibo is a small town.

______ 3. In Caracas there are no high-rise buildings.

______ 4. People in the slums of Caracas live in shacks called *shabonos.*

______ 5. The people with more money prefer to live in the business district.

______ 6. Members of the Yanomami tribe live in communal housing.

______ 7. Many homes in Venezuela have a *chinchorro* for resting on the patio.

Nombre: ______________________ Fecha: ____________

9 La comida venezolana

Pablo wants to cook some typical Venezuelan food, but he mixed up the ingredients. Help him by writing the following ingredients under the appropriate column.

carne	arroz	agua	frijoles negros
harina de maíz	carne	sal	hojas de plátano
aceite	harina de maíz	vegetales	especias

Arepas	Pabellón criollo	Hallacas

Nombre: ______________________________ Fecha: ______________

10 Categorías

Choose the word in each row that does not belong in the group.

MODELO: pan	sopa	(tenedor)	mantequilla
1. cuchillo	postre	tenedor	cuchara
2. plato	vaso	taza	pimienta
3. sal	cucharita	pimienta	azúcar
4. sopa	agua	leche	cubiertos
5. estufa	mantel	servilleta	plato
6. arepa	sopa	pan	taza

11 Ocho diferencias

Look at the two illustrations carefully and find the differences. Write the eight objects that are missing from the second illustration in the spaces provided.

1. ______________________ 5. ______________________

2. ______________________ 6. ______________________

3. ______________________ 7. ______________________

4. ______________________ 8. ______________________

Nombre: ______________________ Fecha: ______________

12 Supermercado González

Read the following advertisement and answer the questions.

1. ¿Cuánto cuesta *(costs)* el pan?

   ____

2. Si tienes 14 pesos, ¿cuántos litros de aceite puedes comprar?

   ____

3. ¿Qué cuesta más: el pan o la sopa?

   ____

4. ¿Qué cubierto necesitas para comer sopa?

   ____

5. ¿Qué comida puedes cocinar con aceite?

   ____

Nombre: ______________________ Fecha: ____________

13 Este...

Write sentences saying where the following things are from, using the correct forms of the demonstrative adjective *este*.

MODELO: servilletas / Guatemala
Estas servilletas son de Guatemala.

1. mantel / España ______________________
2. tazas / Colombia ______________________
3. cubiertos / Perú ______________________
4. estufa / México ______________________
5. plato / Venezuela ______________________
6. lámpara / Chile ______________________

14 Pásame ese...

Use the illustrations and the correct forms of the demonstrative adjective ese to say what you want passed.

MODELO: Pásame esa cuchara.

1. ______________________
2. ______________________
3. ______________________
4. ______________________
5. ______________________
6. ______________________

Nombre: ____ Fecha: ________________

15 Aquel...

Complete the following paragraph with the correct forms of the demonstrative adjective *aquel.*

(1)__________________ chicos son mis primos. Ellos viven en (2)__________________ casa amarilla. (3)__________________ señora es mi tía. Ella trabaja en (4)__________________ restaurante de allá. Ella prepara las arepas. ¡(5)__________________ arepas son riquísimas!

16 En un restaurante

Imagine you are at a restaurant with Ramiro, a friend who complains about everything. Complete the sentences with the appropriate forms of *este*, *ese* or *aquel*, based upon the point of view of Ramiro.

1. _______________ sopa no está caliente.
2. _______________ pan sí está caliente.
3. _______________ servilletas son viejas.
4. _______________ mesa no tiene mantel.
5. _______________ chicos comen mucho.
6. Me gustaría comer _______________ postre.
7. _______________ vasos están sucios.
8. Los vasos de _______________ mesa están limpios.

Nombre: ______________________ Fecha: __________

Lección B

1 Plano de la casa

A. Look at the following floor plan and label the rooms: *baño*, *cocina*, *comedor*, *cuarto*, *garaje*, *patio* and *sala*.

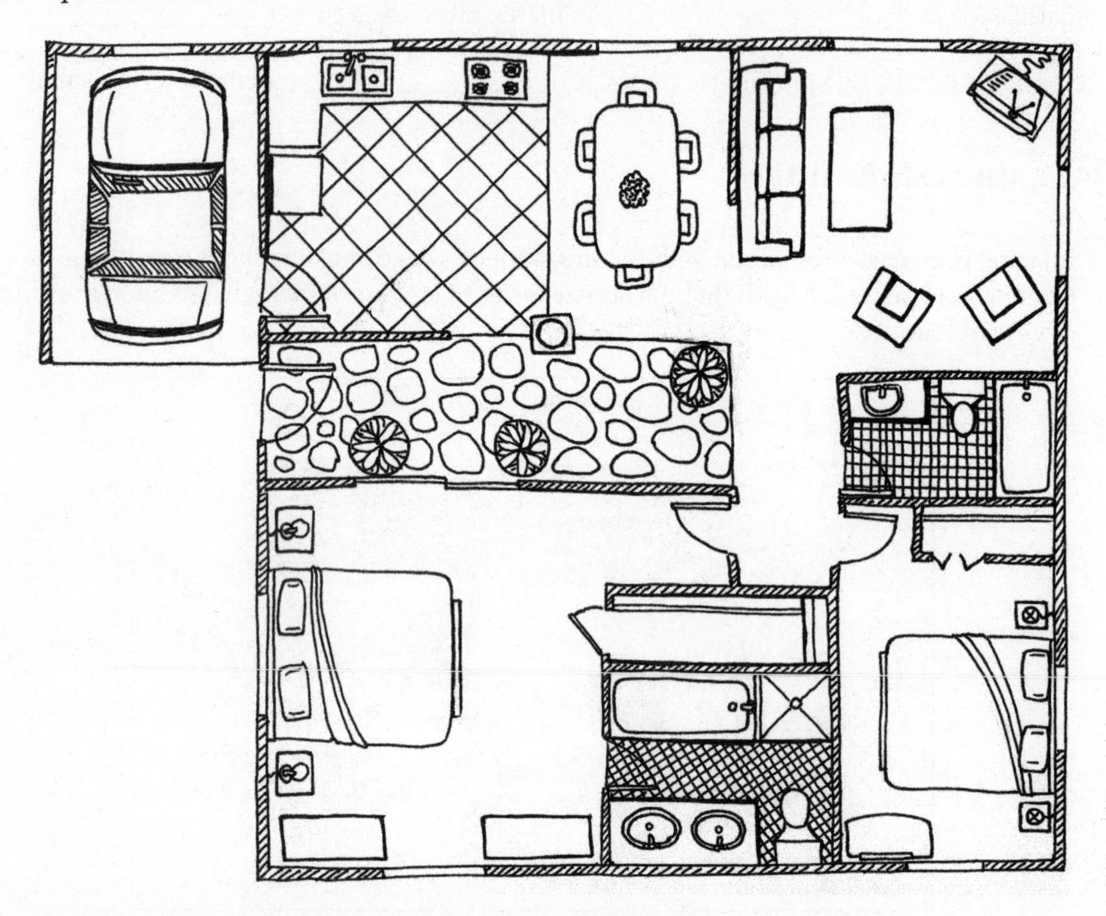

B. Read the following statements and decide whether they are *cierto* (true) or *falso* (false), based upon the floor plan above. Write **C** or **F** in the space provided.

_______ 1. La casa tiene dos baños.

_______ 2. Los cuartos están en el primer piso.

_______ 3. El garaje es muy grande.

_______ 4. La cocina está cerca del baño.

_______ 5. La sala está al lado del comedor.

_______ 6. La televisión está en el cuarto.

_______ 7. La casa no tiene escaleras.

_______ 8. Los cuartos están cerca del patio.

Nombre: ______________________ Fecha: ____________

2 Sopa de letras

In the word square below, find and circle eight words used to describe the different parts of a house. The words may read horizontally, vertically or diagonally.

S	T	A	I	R	S	C	H	A	O
C	C	H	P	G	B	U	Z	W	S
X	O	B	N	M	A	A	P	I	A
Q	C	M	C	R	E	R	W	O	L
U	I	D	E	G	H	T	A	P	A
E	N	R	R	D	I	O	L	J	L
P	A	T	I	O	O	M	L	S	E
I	X	N	T	Y	W	R	P	K	H
S	Ñ	O	B	A	Ñ	O	W	C	V
O	Y	U	I	O	B	N	M	R	T

3 ¿Dónde está?

Say in what part of the house Ignacio is, based on his clues.

MODELO: Pongo la mesa.
Está en el comedor.

1. Cierro la puerta del refrigerador.

   ____

2. Monto al carro.

   ____

3. Busco mis zapatos.

   ____

4. Canto en la ducha *(shower)*.

   ____

5. Veo muchas plantas.

   ____

6. Hablo con los amigos de mis padres.

   ____

Nombre: ______________________________ Fecha: ______________

4 Dicen

What are the people in the illustration saying? Complete the sentences, using the appropriate form of the verb *decir*.

MODELO: 

Tomás dice: "¡Hola!".

Aló.

1. Daniela 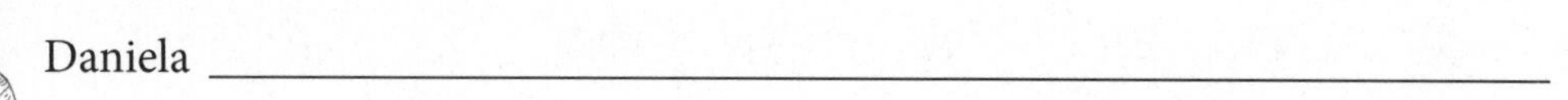

Por favor.

2. Yo ______________________________

¡Qué grande!

3. Diana y Mario ______________________________

Prefiero caminar.

4. Matilde ______________________________

5. Luisito y Sara ______________________________

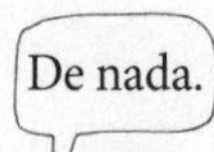

6. Doña Carla ______________________________

7. Julio y yo ______________________________

8. Ricardo ______________________________

Nombre: ______________________________ Fecha: ______________

5 ¿Qué dicen?

Complete the following sentences, using the appropriate forms of the verb *decir.*

1. Mi hermano ______________ que no le gusta escribir.
2. Mis primos ______________ que ellos prefieren hablar por teléfono.
3. Carlota ______________ que la casa es muy pequeña.
4. Yo ______________ que la casa es cómoda.
5. Mi hermano y yo ______________ que nos gustaría ir a Cali.
6. Tú siempre ______________ que te gustaría ir de compras.

6 ¿Qué dice el periódico?

Look at the following newspaper ad. Then answer the questions, telling what the ad says.

MODELO: ¿Tienen las casas closets?
Sí, dice que tienen closets.

1. ¿Hay casas de dos plantas?

____

2. ¿Cuántos baños tienen las casas?

____

3. ¿Cuántos cuartos, o recámaras, tienen las casas?

____

4. ¿Cuánto es la mensualidad *(monthly payment)*?

____

Nombre: ______________________________ Fecha: ______________

7 Colombia

You are looking for some information about Colombia before your next trip to that country. Imagine you found the following information online about Colombia's architecture, but some words are missing. Complete the paragraph with the words from the list.

africano-americana	Caribe	inglesa
apartamentos	clima	pisos
Bogotá	colonial	porche

La arquitectura de Colombia está determinada por su (1) ______________ y diversidad cultural. Las casas de Cartagena, en la costa del (2) ______________, conservan el estilo (3) ______________. Las casas son grandes, de dos (4) ______________, con colores alegres. En las ciudades grandes, como (5) ______________, mucha gente vive en (6) ______________. Los espacios son más pequeños, pero siempre hay sitio para plantas y flores. Las construcciones de San Andrés tienen influencia (7) ______________ y (8) ______________. Las casas tienen un (9) ______________. Aquí la gente descansa (*rest*) y disfruta (*enjoy*) del aire fresco.

Nombre: ______________________________ Fecha: ______________

8 Mi casa en Colombia

Imagine you have moved to Colombia. In the space provided, draw a picture of the colonial-style house where you live. Then, write a paragraph describing the house, focusing on the patio. Use the information you have learned in this lesson.

Nombre: ______________________________ Fecha: ______________

9 ¿Qué tienen?

What are the following people saying, according to the illustrations? Fill in the speech bubbles with *Tengo* and the nouns *calor, frío, ganas de, hambre, miedo, prisa, sed* and *sueño.*

MODELO:

1. 

2. 

3. 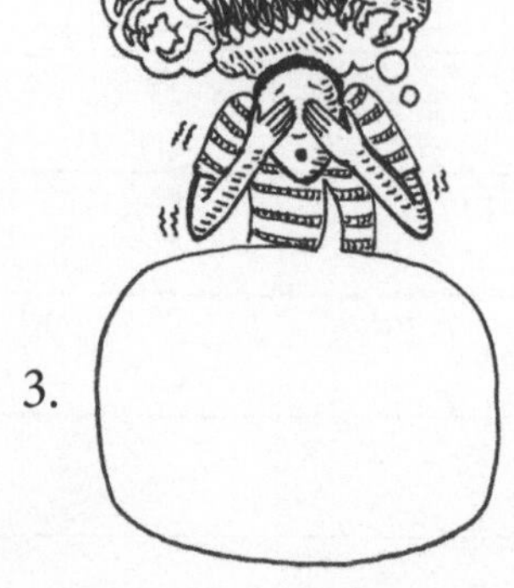

4. 

5. 

6. 

7. 

8. 

Nombre: ______________________________ Fecha: ______________

10 Definiciones

Complete the definitions, using the words from the list.

hambre mentira perdón prestada repito sed

1. Si no digo la verdad, digo una ______________________.
2. Si quiero comer, tengo ______________________.
3. Si digo "Lo siento", pido ______________________.
4. Si digo lo que tú dices, ______________________ lo que dices.
5. Si tengo ______________________, tomo agua.
6. Si quiero la bicicleta de mi hermano, pido ______________________ su bicicleta.

11 No es verdad

Say that the following statements are not true by stating the opposite of the underlined words. Follow the model.

MODELO: La abuela tiene <u>mucho tiempo</u>.
<u>No es verdad. La abuela tiene prisa.</u>

1. Jimena prefiere una casa <u>pequeña</u>.

____

2. Yolanda tiene <u>mucha</u> hambre.

____

3. Cartagena está <u>cerca</u>.

____

4. Pablo debe <u>abrir</u> las ventanas.

____

5. Gilberto tiene <u>frío</u>.

____

Nombre: ______________________________ Fecha: ______________

12 Una carta de Medellín

Complete the following letter with the correct forms of the verbs in parentheses.

Querida Érica,

¿Cómo estás? Yo estoy bien. Ahora (1. vivir) ____________ *con mis abuelos en Medellín, Colombia. Mis abuelos* (2. tener) ____________ *una casa grande.*

Ellos (3. pensar) ____________ *comprar un apartamento pero yo*

(4. preferir) ____________ *vivir en esta casa. Las ventanas no*

(5. cerrar) ____________ *bien y hay luces que no* (6. encender) ____________

pero tiene "carácter". Todas las noches, mis abuelos y yo

(7. comer) ____________ *en el patio. Después,* (8. salir) ____________

a la plaza y allí (9. hablar) ____________ *con los amigos.*

Érica, ¿por qué no (10. escribir) ____________ *o* (11. llamar) ____________

por teléfono?

Te quiero,

Armando

13 Repite mucho

Complete the following paragraph with the correct forms of the verb *repetir*.

Yo no (1) ______________ lo que mis amigos dicen porque no me gustan las personas

que (2) ______________ todo. Mi amigo, Víctor, (3) ______________ mucho.

Si yo digo "Fantástico", él (4) ______________ "Fantástico". ¿Piensas que si mis amigos

y yo (5) ______________ lo que Víctor dice, él no va a repetir más? ¿Y tú?

¿(6) ______________ lo que tus amigos dicen o no?

Nombre: ______________________________ Fecha: ______________

14 ¿Qué piden?

Say what everyone orders at the restaurant, using the cues and the appropriate form of the verb *pedir*.

MODELO: Leonor / agua mineral
Leonor pide agua mineral.

1. yo / sopa de pollo ______________________________
2. los chicos / postre ______________________________
3. la Sra. Duarte / ensalada ______________________________
4. tú / pan con mantequilla ______________________________
5. nosotros / arepas ______________________________
6. Guillermo / jugo de naranja ______________________________
7. Carlos y Elena / pescado ______________________________
8. Paco y yo / hallacas ______________________________

15 *Pedir* y *preguntar*

Complete the following sentences with the correct forms of *pedir* or *preguntar*, whichever is appropriate.

1. Verónica ______________ prestado un mantel porque no tiene uno.
2. La abuela ______________ por qué Verónica necesita un mantel.
3. Los amigos ______________ a qué hora es la fiesta.
4. Eduardo ______________ perdón porque no tiene ganas de salir.
5. Nosotros ______________: "¿Qué tienes?".
6. Verónica y Nuria ______________ ayuda en la cocina.
7. Yo ______________ un vaso de agua fría.
8. Tú ______________ permiso para ir al baño.
9. Hernán ______________ dónde está el baño.
10. Jaime dice una mentira y después ______________ perdón.

Nombre: ______________________________ Fecha: ______________

Unidad 7

Lección A

1 Crucigrama

Complete the following crossword puzzle with words used for pastimes.

Horizontal

1. Para jugar a las ___, necesitas fichas *(counters)* rojas y negras.
3. Nintendo® hace muchos ___.
4. El fútbol ___ es diferente que el fútbol *(soccer)*.
6. Necesitas una pelota *(ball)* y una canasta *(hoop)* para jugar al ___.
7. Si tienes un A❤ o un 5◆ , juegas a las ___.
8. Un ___ es una actividad divertida.

Vertical

1. Necesitas papel y lápices de color para ___.
2. Si una pieza es un caballo, juegas al ___.
4. Los ___ son ejercicios que haces con música.
5. Para jugar al ___, le das a la pelota *(ball)* con las manos o los brazos.

Nombre: ______________________ Fecha: ____________

2 ¿Qué te gusta hacer?

Say if you like or you do not like to do the illustrated activities. Follow the model.

MODELO:  Me (No me) gusta jugar al fútbol americano.

1. 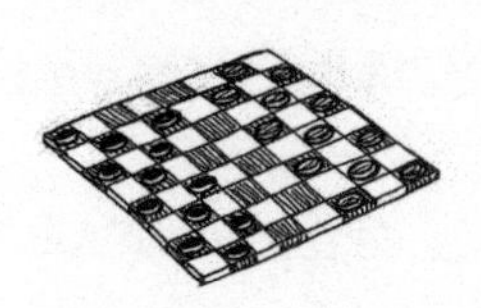

____

____

2. 

____

____

3. 

____

____

4. 

____

____

5. 

____

____

6. 

____

____

7. 

____

____

8. 

____

____

Nombre: ______________________ Fecha: ____________

3 Una familia atlética

Complete the following paragraph with the appropriate forms of the verb *jugar*.

A mi familia le gusta mucho jugar. Todos los sábados, mi hermana Raquel

(1)____________ al básquetbol. Mis padres (2)____________ a las cartas, yo

(3)____________ al ajedrez y mis primos (4)____________ al fútbol.

Por la noche, mis hermanos y yo (5)____________ a los videojuegos. Y tú, ¿a qué

(6)____________ los sábados?

4 ¡Vamos a Argentina!

Look at the following ad for trips around Argentina and answer the questions.

1. ¿Cuánto cuesta ir a Iguazú?

____

2. ¿Cuánto cuesta ir a Bariloche?

____

3. ¿Adónde puedes ir por $439?

____

4. ¿Adónde puedes ir por $569?

____

Nombre: ______________________ Fecha: ______________

5 ¿Quién puede ir?

Complete the sentences to say who can and cannot go on a trip to Bariloche.

Sí va a Bariloche	No va a Bariloche
yo	Roxana
Ana	Sr. Valdez
Teresa	Carlos
tú	Víctor
Samuel	Luis

MODELO: Roxana no puede ir.

1. Carlos ______________________.
2. Yo ______________________.
3. Teresa ______________________.
4. Víctor y Luis ______________________.
5. Ana y yo ______________________.
6. El Sr. Valdez ______________________.
7. Tú ______________________.
8. Samuel y yo ______________________.

Nombre: ______________________________ Fecha: ______________

6 ¿Cuándo vuelven?

Use the cues and the appropriate form of the verb *volver* to write complete sentences, saying when everyone returns from the trip.

MODELO: Ana / sábado
Ana vuelve el sábado.

1. yo / sábado ______________________________
2. tú / domingo ______________________________
3. Teresa / jueves ______________________________
4. Ana y yo / sábado ______________________________
5. Samuel / martes ______________________________
6. mis tíos / viernes ______________________________
7. Raúl y Laura / lunes ______________________________
8. Hugo / miércoles ______________________________

7 Argentina

Choose the best completion for each statement about Argentina.

1. Las cataratas de Iguazú están en la región subtropical del…

   A. sur B. oeste C. norte

2. La provincia de Mendoza está cerca…

   A. de Buenos Aires B. de los Andes C. del Río de la Plata

3. El mate es una infusión que se toma…

   A. en taza B. con una cuchara C. con una bombilla

4. La chacarera es…

   A. una bebida tradicional B. un baile folclórico C. un parque nacional

5. Los gauchos viven en…

   A. las estancias de las pampas B. las montañas de los Andes C. la costa del océano Atlántico

Nombre: ______________________________ Fecha: ______________

8 Una visita a Argentina

Imagine you went to Argentina during the summer, and now you are on social media chatting about your trip with a member of your family. Answer the questions of the person online.

1. ¿Cómo es Argentina?

____

2. ¿Cómo es la ciudad de Buenos Aires?

____

____

____

3. ¿Qué actividades puedes hacer en la Reserva Ecológica de Buenos Aires?

____

____

4. ¿Qué hacen los porteños en la Costanera?

____

____

5. ¿Por qué es famoso el nombre Caminito?

____

____

Nombre: ______________________________ Fecha: ______________

9 ¡Vamos!

Complete the following conversation with the words from the list.

alquilar	apagar	casi	control remoto	dormir
estupendo	mismo	segundo	siglos	

ERNESTO: Hola, Eugenia. ¿Qué hora es?

EUGENIA: Son las doce menos diez. Es (1)______________ mediodía.

ERNESTO: ¿Dónde está Memo?

EUGENIA: Está en su cuarto. Quiere (2)______________ porque está muy cansado.

ERNESTO: ¿Quieres ir a (3)______________ una película?

EUGENIA: Sí, (4)______________. Hace (5)______________ que no veo una película. ¿Cuándo quieres ir?

ERNESTO: Vamos ahora (6)______________.

EUGENIA: Un (7)______________. Primero debo (8)______________ la televisión. ¿Dónde está el (9)______________?

ERNESTO: Aquí está. ¡Vamos!

10 El tiempo

Rewrite the following periods of time in order, from shortest to longest.

minuto	siglo	mes	año
semana	día	hora	segundo

______________ → ______________ → ______________ →

______________ → ______________ → ______________ →

______________ → ______________

Nombre: ______________________ Fecha: ____________

11 ¿Cuánto tiempo?

Using the cues, write questions asking how long has it been since these people did the following things. Follow the model.

MODELO: Vicente / jugar a las damas
¿Cuánto tiempo hace que Vicente no juega a las damas?

1. Silvia / alquilar una película

____

2. tú / jugar al voleibol

____

3. Lola y Paco / correr

____

4. Juanita / hacer aeróbicos

____

5. nosotros / viajar

____

12 Hace mucho tiempo

Now answer the questions from Activity 10, using the following cues.

MODELO: mucho tiempo
Hace mucho tiempo que Vicente no juega a las damas.

1. un mes

____

2. tres días

____

3. una semana

____

4. mucho tiempo

____

5. un año

____

Nombre: ______________________________ Fecha: ______________

13 Están haciendo muchas cosas

Say what the following people are doing right now, based upon the drawing. Write complete sentences, using the present progressive.

MODELO: Rosario
Rosario está haciendo aeróbicos.

1. el Sr. Torres ______________________________
2. tú ______________________________
3. doña Petra ______________________________
4. Ricardo ______________________________
5. don Pablo ______________________________
6. los chicos ______________________________
7. nosotros ______________________________

Nombre: ______________________________ Fecha: ______________

14 ¿Estás haciéndolo?

Answer the following questions affirmatively, in two different ways: first, by placing the direct-object pronoun before the verb, and second, by attaching the direct-object pronoun to the verb form. Follow the model.

MODELO: ¿Estás haciendo las tareas?
Sí, las estoy haciendo. / Sí, estoy haciéndolas.

1. ¿Estás poniendo la mesa?

____

____

2. ¿Estás alquilando las mismas películas?

____

____

3. ¿Estás leyendo el periódico?

____

____

4. ¿Estás tomando el jugo de naranja?

____

____

5. ¿Estás viendo la telenovela?

____

____

6. ¿Estás celebrando tu cumpleaños?

____

____

7. ¿Estás llamando a tus amigos?

____

____

8. ¿Estás comprendiendo el español?

____

____

Nombre: ______________________________ Fecha: ______________

Lección B

1 ¿Qué estación es?

Look at the following drawings and read the statements. Write the letter of the drawing that matches the statement in the space provided.

A.

B.

C.

D.

______ 1. Es verano.

______ 2. Llueve.

______ 3. Hay muchas flores.

______ 4. Está montando en patineta.

______ 5. Está patinando sobre hielo.

______ 6. Hace frío.

______ 7. Está dando un paseo por la playa.

______ 8. Es otoño.

______ 9. Es primavera.

______ 10. Hace mucho calor.

______ 11. Es invierno.

______ 12. Hace sol.

2 El tiempo y tú

Complete the following statements.

1. Cuando hace sol, me gusta ______________________________.
2. Cuando hace frío, mis amigos prefieren ______________________________.
3. En julio no podemos esquiar en Colorado pero en cambio podemos esquiar en ______________________________.
4. Cuando hace mucho calor, yo ______________________________.
5. Donde vivo, el mes de ______________________________ llueve más.

Nombre: ______________________ Fecha: ______________

3 Las estaciones en Chile

Find and circle the four seasons of the year and three activities you can do during these seasons in the word square below. The words may read vertically, horizontally or diagonally.

J	S	N	V	E	R	A	N	O	S	I
A	E	N	O	M	S	R	E	A	E	N
O	T	O	Ñ	O	A	W	V	B	S	V
E	E	W	M	N	O	B	B	R	Q	I
A	Q	N	I	U	I	R	L	I	U	E
G	U	T	E	V	R	E	A	L	I	R
O	A	S	E	R	G	R	M	B	A	N
P	R	I	M	A	V	E	R	A	R	O
T	T	A	L	O	B	T	U	X	R	E
D	A	R	U	N	P	A	S	E	O	E

Nombre: ______________________________ Fecha: ______________

4 Mis amigos y yo

Complete each sentence with the appropriate form of the verb in parentheses.

1. Mis amigos y yo ____________________ en Farellones. (esquiar)
2. Beatriz ____________________ muy bien. (esquiar)
3. Tú ____________________ flores a tu abuela, ¿verdad? (enviar)
4. Nosotros ____________________ estudiando español. (continuar)
5. Daniel ____________________ la lista de palabras nuevas. (copiar)
6. ¿____________________ tú jugando a los videojuegos? (continuar)
7. Laura y Tobías te ____________________ muchos saludos. (enviar)

5 Un e-mail

Complete the following e-mail with the appropriate forms of the verbs from the list.

copiar continuar enviar esquiar saber tener

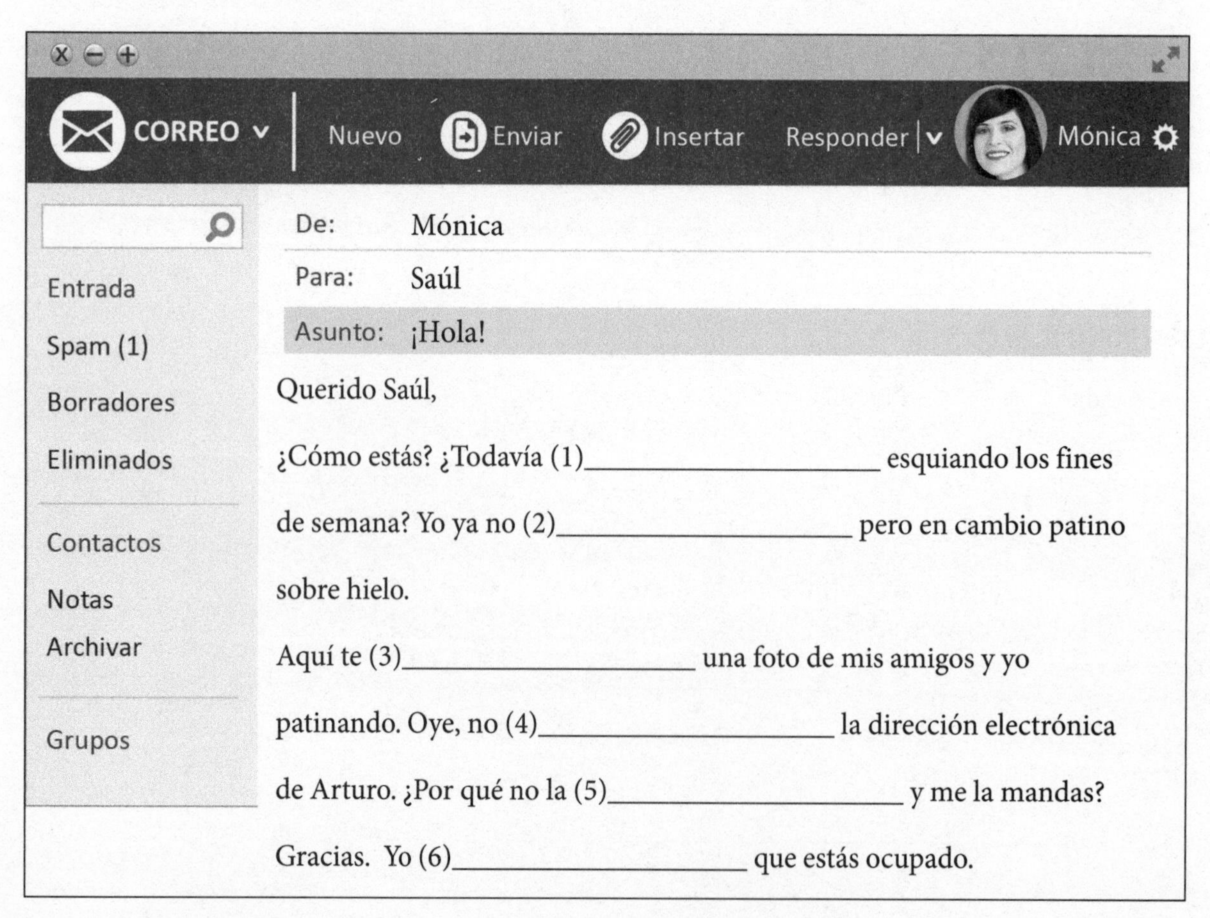

De: Mónica

Para: Saúl

Asunto: ¡Hola!

Querido Saúl,

¿Cómo estás? ¿Todavía (1)____________________ esquiando los fines de semana? Yo ya no (2)____________________ pero en cambio patino sobre hielo.

Aquí te (3)____________________ una foto de mis amigos y yo patinando. Oye, no (4)____________________ la dirección electrónica de Arturo. ¿Por qué no la (5)____________________ y me la mandas?

Gracias. Yo (6)____________________ que estás ocupado.

Nombre: ______________________ Fecha: __________

6 Contesta

Answer the following questions, using complete sentences.

1. ¿A qué hora sales de la casa por la mañana?

____

2. ¿En qué cuarto de la casa haces las tareas de la escuela?

____

3. ¿Cuánto tiempo hace que no pones la mesa en casa?

____

4. ¿Cuántas horas de televisión ves en una semana?

____

5. ¿Por dónde das paseos con tus amigos/as?

____

6. ¿Sabes patinar sobre hielo?

____

7 ¿Qué haces?

Combine elements from each column to write six complete sentences with the pronoun *yo*.

MODELO: Yo patino sobre hielo en invierno.

patinar	la maleta	en patineta
dar	sobre hielo	por la puerta
poner	montar	por la playa
hacer	de la casa	en el cine
saber	flores	por toda la casa
salir	un paseo	antes de viajar
ver	una película	en invierno

1. ______________________
2. ______________________
3. ______________________
4. ______________________
5. ______________________
6. ______________________

Nombre: ______________________________ Fecha: ______________

8 Chile

Read the following statements about Chile and decide whether they are *cierto* (true) or *falso* (false). Write **C** or **F** in the space provided.

______ 1. La ciudad de Santiago tiene 50 % de la población de Chile.

______ 2. Chile está rodeado por barreras naturales que lo separan del océano.

______ 3. El desierto de Atacama es ideal para practicar rally.

______ 4. La costa de Chile tiene unos 4.000 km.

______ 5. Las personas van a Pichilemu a esquiar.

______ 6. En Chile, no se practica surf porque no hay mucho viento.

______ 7. En Chile, hay ríos y mar, pero no hay lagos.

______ 8. Se practica el rodeo en un estadio semicircular llamado *medialuna*.

9 Los paisajes de Chile

Choose the correct answer to complete the following statements. Write the answer in the space provided.

______ 1. La ciudad de Portillo está…
A. en la costa del Pacífico
B. cerca de Argentina
C. en el sur de Chile

______ 2. Las características geográficas de Chile…
A. no son buenas para practicar deporte
B. no son muy atractivas para el turismo internacional
C. permiten hacer muchas actividades al aire libre

______ 3. El palín es una actividad tradicional de las comunidades…
A. del norte de Chile
B. del centro de Chile
C. del sur de Chile

______ 4. El juego del palín…
A. es similar al hockey
B. no se juega en tiempos modernos
C. tiene su origen en Canadá

______ 5. El deporte que incluye una ceremonia religiosa con baile y comida es…
A. el palín
B. el fútbol
C. el rodeo

______ 6. Además del rodeo, los chilenos de todo el país disfrutan del…
A. surf
B. fútbol
C. rafting

Nombre: ______________________ Fecha: ____________

10 El tiempo en Chile

What is the weather like in Chile? Look at the following newspaper clipping and answer the questions.

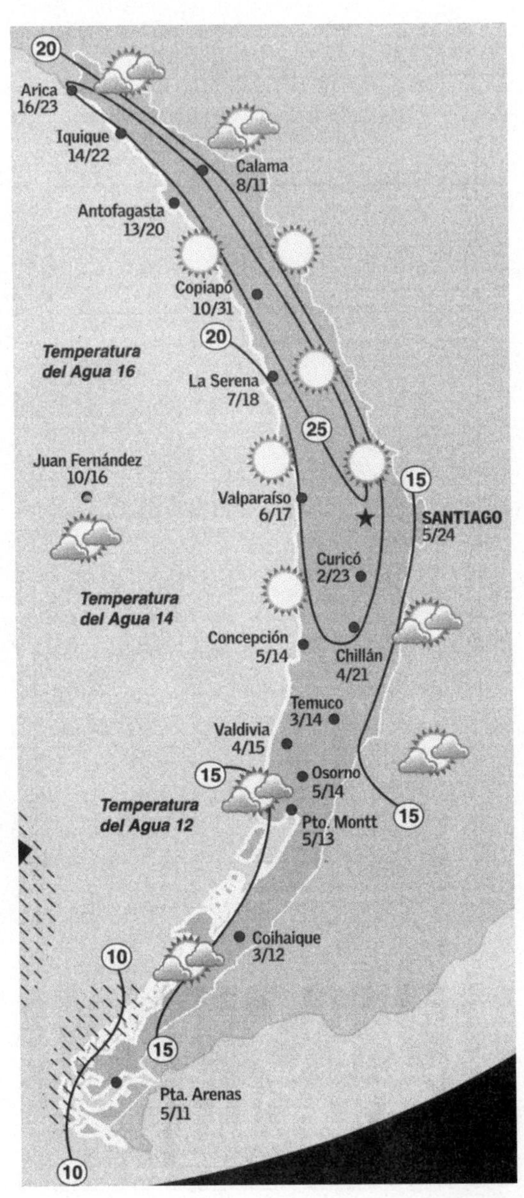

1. ¿Cuál es la temperatura máxima de Santiago?

____

____

2. ¿Cuál es la temperatura mínima de Juan Fernández?

____

____

3. ¿Está soleado en Arica?

____

____

4. ¿Qué tiempo hace en Punta Arenas?

____

____

5. ¿Qué tiempo hace en Valparaíso?

____

____

Nombre: ______________________________ Fecha: ______________

11 ¿Qué tiempo hace?

For each drawing, write one sentence describing the weather.

MODELO:  Hace sol.

1. ______________________________

4. ______________________________

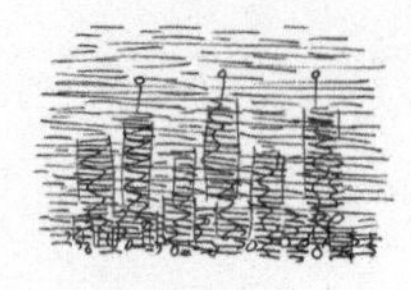

2. ______________________________

5. ______________________________

3. ______________________________

12 ¿Qué temperatura hace?

Look at the list of cities around the world and their high temperature in degrees centigrade. Decide whether it's hot, cold or mild. Write *Hace calor*, *Hace frío* or *Hace fresco* in the space provided.

1. Madrid 2°C ______________________
2. Panamá 33°C ______________________
3. Managua 31°C ______________________
4. La Paz 21°C ______________________
5. Santiago 31°C ______________________
6. Nueva York 4°C ______________________
7. Bogotá 19°C ______________________
8. Los Ángeles 17°C ______________________

Nombre: ______________________________ Fecha: ______________

13 Deportistas

Look at each drawing and decide what kind of athlete each person is. Write a complete sentence, naming the person who participates in that sport. Follow the model.

MODELO:  Armando es patinador.

1. Pedro y Orlando 

____

____

2. Selena 

____

____

3. las hermanas Franco 

____

____

4. Miguel 

____

____

5. Maira y Olga 

____

____

6. Octavio 

____

____

7. Sarita 

____

____

8. mis primos 

____

____

Nombre: ______________________________ Fecha: ______________

14 ¿En qué lugar?

The following newspaper clipping shows the results of a bicycle race in Buenos Aires, Argentina. Complete the sentences that follow with the appropriate ordinal numbers. Follow the model.

MODELO: Eddy Cisneros llega en cuarto lugar.

La clasificación general

Categoría élite		(120 km)	
Pos.	**Ciclista**	**Equipo**	**Tiempo**
1º	Pedro Prieto	Imperial Cord	**2h49m**
2º	Leandro Missineo	Tres de Febrero	**m.t.**
3º	Anibal Alborcen	Keops	**m.t.**
4º	Eddy Cisneros	Coach	**m.t.**
5º	Darío Piñeiro	Tres Arroyos	**m.t.**
6º	Franco Byllo	Bancalari	**m.t.**
7º	David Kenig	Tres de Febrero	**m.t.**
8º	Luis Lorenz	Tres de Febrero	**m.t.**
9º	Daniel Capella	Tres de Febrero	**m.t.**
10º	Gastón Corsaro	Tres Arroyos	**m.t.**

Promedio del ganardor: 42 km/ h.

1. Pedro Prieto llega en ______________________________ lugar.
2. Gastón Corsaro llega en ______________________________ lugar.
3. Darío Piñeiro llega en ______________________________ lugar.
4. Franco Byllo llega en ______________________________ lugar.
5. Leandro Missineo llega en ______________________________ lugar.
6. Daniel Capella llega en ______________________________ lugar.
7. Anibal Alborcen llega en ______________________________ lugar.
8. Luis Lorenz llega en ______________________________ lugar.
9. David Kenig llega en ______________________________ lugar.

Nombre: ______________________ Fecha: ____________

15 Primeros en los Juegos Olímpicos

Spanish-speaking countries have always participated in the Olympic Games. Complete the following sentences with the appropriate form of *primer* to learn about their accomplishments.

1. Chile fue el único *(only)* país latinoamericano que participó en los ____________ Juegos Olímpicos modernos en 1896.
2. El argentino Delfo Cabrera fue el corredor que llegó en ____________ lugar en el maratón en 1948.
3. En 1972, el cubano Alberto Juantorena fue el ____________ corredor en terminar los 400 metros y los 800 metros.
4. En 1996, la costarricense Claudia Poll fue la ____________ nadadora en terminar los 200 metros.
5. Jefferson Pérez fue el ____________ deportista de Ecuador en ganar *(win)* una medalla de oro en 1996.
6. Soraya Jiménez Mendivil ganó *(won)* una medalla de oro en el 2000, la ____________ mujer *(woman)* mexicana en hacerlo.

16 ¿Qué mes es?

Answer the following questions in complete sentences.

1. ¿Cuál es el primer mes del año?

   ____

2. ¿Cuál es el octavo mes del año?

   ____

3. ¿Cuál es el tercer mes del año?

   ____

4. ¿Cuál es el quinto mes del año?

   ____

Nombre: ______________________ Fecha: ____________

Unidad 8

Lección A

1 ¿Qué están haciendo?

Look at the following drawing. Write what each family member is doing right now to help with the housework.

Modelo: Andrés está limpiando el baño.

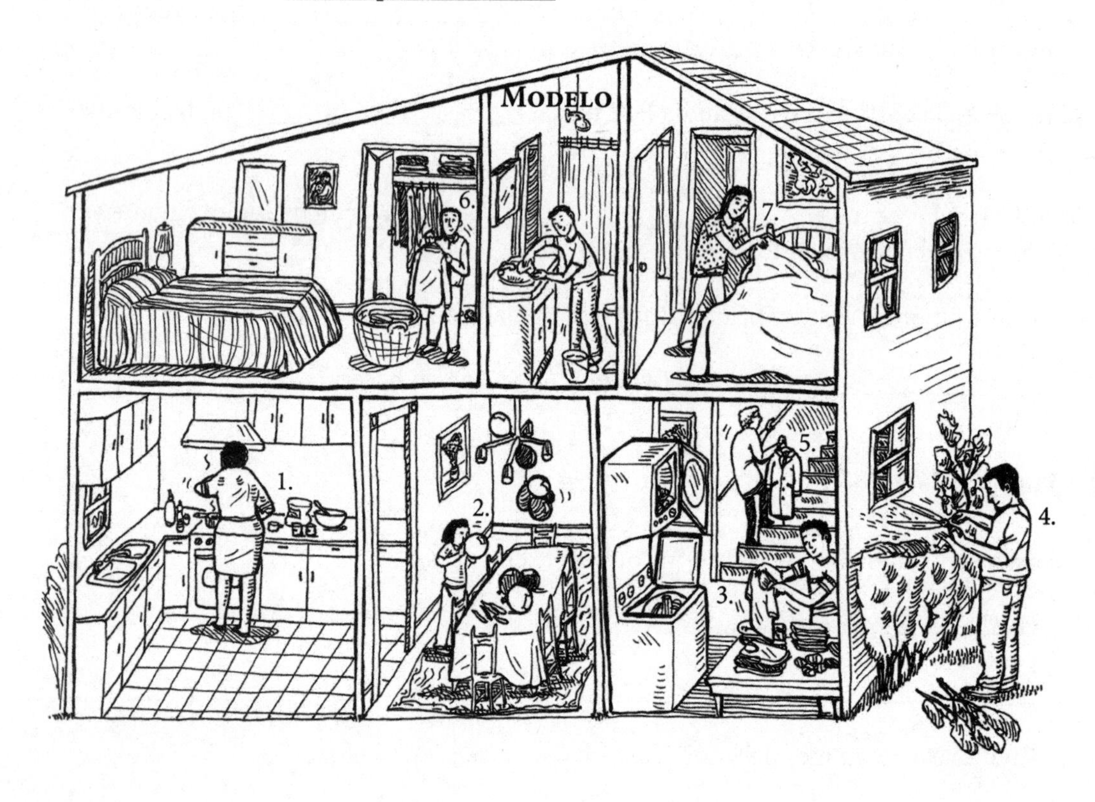

1. La señora Rojas ______________________
2. Mariana ______________________
3. Gustavo ______________________
4. El señor Rojas ______________________
5. Doña Elmira ______________________
6. Raúl ______________________
7. Rosario ______________________

Nombre: ______________________________ Fecha: ______________

2 Pronombres de complemento directo

Complete each sentence with the appropriate *pronombre de complemento directo.*

MODELO: Voy a comprar una revista y la voy a leer.

1. Víctor ve el abrigo y ________ compra.
2. Yo siempro lavo la ropa y ________ doblo.
3. Pintamos la pared y luego ________ adornamos.
4. Los estudiantes miran las palabras y ________ copian.
5. Vero va a alquilar tres películas y ________ va a ver esta noche.
6. ¿Por qué no compramos un nuevo disco compacto y ________ escuchamos?
7. Héctor hace las maletas y Sonia ________ abre.

3 Pronombres de complemento indirecto

Complete the sentences with the correct indirect-object pronouns.

MODELO: ¿Les preparas la comida a tus hermanos?

1. Mañana, ______ voy a lavar el carro a papá.
2. Mario ______ prepara a nosotros una comida especial.
3. Paloma ______ sube a la abuela el café.
4. Rodrigo ______ escribe una carta, pero tú no contestas.
5. Mamá ______ limpia el cuarto a los niños.
6. Yo ______ lavo la ropa a Joaquín y él ______ la dobla.

Nombre: ______________________________ Fecha: ______________

4 Otra vez

Rewrite the following sentences by moving the indirect-object pronoun to another position.

MODELO: ¿Me puedes subir el abrigo? / ¿Puedes subirme el abrigo?

1. Le estoy leyendo el periódico al abuelo.

    ____

2. Quiero enviarte un correo electrónico.

    ____

3. ¿Puedes alquilarme una película divertida?

    ____

4. Les debes ayudar a tus padres en casa.

    ____

5. Te estamos limpiando el cuarto.

    ____

6. Esta noche voy a adornarle la casa a Carlota.

    ____

7. ¿Por qué no nos quieres cantar una canción?

    ____

8. Queremos celebrarle el cumpleaños a la profesora.

    ____

9. Les estoy dejando mi estéreo.

    ____

Nombre: ______________________ Fecha: ____________

5 ¿A quién le compras?

Imagine you have a gift certificate for the bookstore Universal. Look at some of the books on sale. Make a list of five books you will buy your family members and friends. Make sure to use the appropriate object pronoun and *a* followed by a noun to clarify to whom you are referring.

Modelo: Le compro *Silabario Castellano* a mi hermanita.

1. ______________________

2. ______________________

3. ______________________

4. ______________________

5. ______________________

Nombre: ______________________ Fecha: ____________

6 ¿Qué acaban de hacer?

Combine elements from each column to write six complete sentences with the appropriate form of the verb *acabar de.*

MODELO: Uds. acaban de adornar la sala.

Uds.		adornar	la cocina
yo		hacer	la cama
Lorenzo		preparar	en el jardín
los hermanos	acabar de	doblar	al primer piso
Mónica		limpiar	la comida
tú		trabajar	la ropa
Lola y yo		subir	la sala

1. ______________________

2. ______________________

3. ______________________

4. ______________________

5. ______________________

6. ______________________

Nombre: ____________________ Fecha: ____________

7 La vida en España

Choose the best completion for each statement about everyday life in Spain.

1. La comida más importante y abundante de los españoles es…

   A. el almuerzo

   B. la merienda

   C. la cena

2. Después del trabajo, muchas personas…

   A. van directo a casa

   B. salen a comer algo

   C. duermen la siesta

3. En España la cena es…

   A. entre las 14:00 y las 16:00

   B. entre las 19:00 y las 20:00

   C. entre las 21:00 y las 22:00

4. En España…

   A. los hijos viven con sus padres hasta 18 años

   B. muchos miembros de la familia viven juntos

   C. las mujeres no trabajan fuera de casa

5. En la actualidad, la división de los quehaceres de la casa es…

   A. completamente equitativa (*fair*)

   B. más equitativa que antes

   C. menos equitativa que antes

Nombre: ______________________ Fecha: ______________

8 Los chicos españoles

Look at the list of activities that young people do in Spain. Write a paragraph telling if you do each of them sometimes, always or never (*a veces, siempre, nunca*). End the paragraph by writing a conclusion as to what you like doing in your everyday life.

hacer recados
recoger la mesa
sacar la basura
almorzar en casa
hacer actividades extraescolares
estudiar inglés
estudiar música
practicar deportes
pasar tiempo en las redes sociales
cenar con la familia
hacer la tarea
salir con amigos
dar un paseo por la ciudad
ver una película
ir a un concierto
salir a bailar

Nombre: ______________________ Fecha: ______________

9 Crucigrama

Complete the following crossword puzzle.

Horizontales

1. inteligente
4. Como cereal con _____.
5. Tengo que _____ la aspiradora por la sala.
9. Necesito _____ el cuarto porque está desordenado *(messy)*.
10. Para _____, necesitas una escoba *(broom)*.

Verticales

2. Necesito _____ la basura.
3. Cocinamos sopa en una _____.
6. Después de comer, vamos a _____ la mesa.
7. Debes poner las cosas en su _____.
8. Voy a _____ de comer al perro.

Nombre: ______________________________ Fecha: ______________

10 ¿Qué oyen?

Look at the schedule for Radio Premium. (Notice that the schedule uses the 24-hour clock.) Write complete sentences, using the correct form of the verb *oír* to indicate what program each person listens to at the given time.

MODELO: Diego / 17:00
Diego oye La guitarra hoy.

Radio Premium

10.00: La cantata del domingo.
12.00: Festival Premium.
13.00: Radio Jazz (Carlos Allo).
14.00: Divertimento (Jorge Rocca).
15.00: Rarezas (Carlos Majlis).
17.00: La guitarra hoy (Marcelo Gallardo).
18.00: Música insólita (Ricardo Forno).
20.00: Colección Beethoven.
24:00: Suspendamos todo.
1:00: Trasnoche Premium.

Mhz	Mhz
FM Radio Nacional 96.7	FM 100 99.9
FM Cultura Musical 100.3	LS10 Del Plata 95.1
FM Radio Show 100.7	FM Hit 105.5
F.M Cultura 97.9	FM Premium 103.5
FM Tango 92.7	FM Mega 98.3

1. el abuelo / 13:00
____

2. Eva y Diana / 12:00
____

3. yo / 14:00
____

4. mi hermana / 18:00
____

5. mis amigos y yo / 20:00
____

6. tú / 10:00
____

7. Ángel / 1:00
____

Nombre: ______________________________ Fecha: ______________

11 ¿Qué traen?

Write complete sentences with the correct form of the verb *traer* to say what the following people bring to the party.

MODELO:  Uds. traen los refrescos.

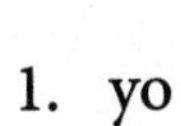
1. yo 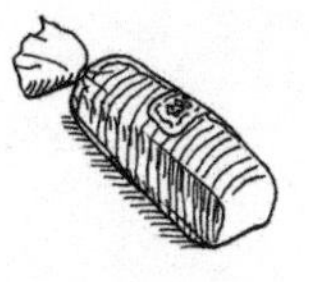

____

____

2. Eduardo 

____

____

3. Anita y Carmen 

____

____

4. tú 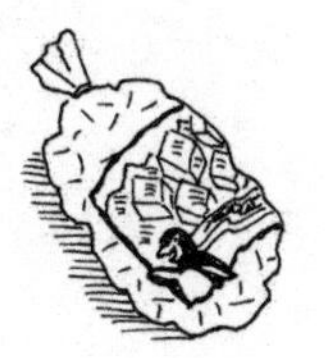

____

____

5. Rubén 

____

____

6. Sergio 

____

____

7. Pilar y yo 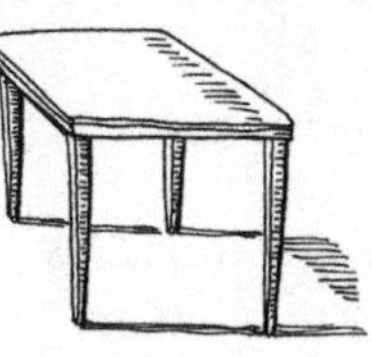

____

____

8. yo 

____

____

Nombre: ______________________________ Fecha: ______________

12 La fiesta de Claudia

Complete the sentences with the preterite forms of the verbs in parentheses.

1. Claudia ____________ a organizar su fiesta hace tres semanas. (empezar)
2. Ella ____________ a veinte personas. (invitar)
3. Sus amigos le ____________ mucho. (ayudar)
4. Conchita ____________ un mapa y lo ____________ con las invitaciones. (dibujar, enviar)
5. Yo ____________ los ingredientes para la comida. (buscar)
6. Yo también ____________ los platos y los cubiertos para poner la mesa. (sacar)
7. Marcos y Norma ____________ la cena. (preparar)
8. Alejandra ____________ y ____________ la sala. (limpiar, adornar)
9. Tú ____________ la aspiradora y ____________ la basura. (pasar, sacar)
10. Cuando las personas ____________, yo ____________ sus abrigos. (llegar, colgar)
11. Después de comer, Marcos ____________ el piano. (tocar)
12. Yo ____________ a cantar y bailar. (empezar)
13. Luego, todas las personas ____________ y ____________. (cantar, bailar)
14. A la medianoche, nosotros ____________ juegos. (buscar)
15. Claudia y unos amigos ____________ a las cartas. (jugar)
16. Yo ____________ a las damas con Marcos. (jugar)
17. Después, tú ____________ unas películas. (alquilar)
18. Yo ____________ las luces y ____________ las ventanas. (apagar, cerrar)
19. Luego, nosotros ____________ películas toda la noche. (mirar)

Nombre: ______________________ Fecha: ______________

Lección B

1 Sopa de letras

Find and circle ten food items in the word square below. The words may read horizontally, vertically or diagonally.

A	S	P	L	E	C	H	U	G	A	Z
G	Y	I	E	Z	A	C	V	B	I	T
U	P	M	M	S	X	R	W	A	H	O
I	C	I	O	T	C	I	R	N	F	M
S	A	E	C	Y	H	A	P	O	E	A
A	Z	N	B	U	I	O	D	P	Z	T
N	J	T	A	O	Q	U	I	O	D	E
T	R	O	P	O	L	L	O	G	H	J
E	S	D	C	V	B	L	M	L	K	E
Z	E	A	G	U	A	C	A	T	E	P

2 Definiciones

Match each word with the corresponding definition. Write the letter of your choice in the space provided.

______ 1. la lata

______ 2. no maduro

______ 3. la receta

______ 4. el supermercado

______ 5. las verduras

A. tienda grande con comida

B. instrucciones para cocinar

C. verde

D. guisantesy pimientos

E. envase *(container)*

Nombre: ______________________________ Fecha: ______________

3 Comparaciones

Write comparing sentences, using *más… que* or *menos… que* and the words given. Make any necessary changes.

MODELO: fiestas / divertido / clases
Las fiestas son más divertidas que las clases.

1. sopa / caliente / ensalada

____

2. tomates rojos / maduro / tomates verdes

____

3. otoño / frío / invierno

____

4. paella / dulce / postre

____

5. avión / rápido / tren

____

6. verduras frescas / sabroso / verduras en lata

____

7. ajo / grande / cebolla

____

8. perros / inteligente / gatos

____

9. ciencias / aburrido / matemáticas

____

10. lechugas / fresco / guisantes en lata

____

Nombre: ______________________________ Fecha: ______________

4 Tienen mucho en común

Read about Clara and Carlos, two twin siblings. Write complete sentences, using *tan/ tanto... como* to summarize what they have in common.

MODELO: Clara tiene un cuarto grande. Carlos tiene un cuarto grande también.
El cuarto de Clara es tan grande como el cuarto de Carlos.

1. Clara tiene muchos amigos. Carlos tiene muchos amigos también.

 ____

2. Clara es simpática. Carlos es simpático también.

 ____

3. Clara tiene cien libros. Carlos tiene cien libros.

 ____

4. Clara corre rápido. Carlos corre rápido también.

 ____

5. Clara juega al básquetbol todos los días. Carlos juega al básquetbol todos los días.

 ____

6. Clara es morena. Carlos es moreno.

 ____

7. Clara va a muchas fiestas. Carlos también va a muchas fiestas.

 ____

8. Clara ayuda con los quehaceres. Carlos ayuda con los quehaceres.

 ____

9. Clara tiene cincuenta discos compactos. Carlos tiene cincuenta discos compactos.

 ____

Nombre: ______________________________ Fecha: ______________

5 Más comparaciones

Complete each sentence by singling out what is talked about. Follow the model.

MODELO: Este supermercado es grande pero aquel supermercado es <u>el supermercado más grande</u> de la ciudad.

1. El restaurante Orozco es bueno pero el restaurante Tamayo es ______________________________ de la ciudad.
2. Manolo corre rápido pero René corre ______________________________ posible.
3. Tú siempre lees bien pero hoy debes leer ______________________________ posible.
4. El Hotel Reyes es un hotel malo pero el Hotel Pulgas es ______________________________ de la ciudad.
5. Teresa es una buena amiga pero Delia es ______________________________ del mundo.
6. Estas verduras están frescas pero aquellas verduras son ______________________________ del mercado.
7. Julio dice que Madrid es una ciudad bonita pero Barcelona es ______________________________ de España.
8. Yo llego al colegio a las ocho pero mañana tengo que llegar ______________________________ posible.
9. Esta película es bastante mala pero aquella película es ______________________________ que alquilamos.
10. Tu plato está sucio pero mi plato es ______________________________ de la mesa.

Nombre: ______________________ Fecha: __________

6 Humberto y Rogelio

Complete each comparison with an appropriate expression from the list. Some expressions will be used more than once.

más de	más grande	más pequeña	más pequeño
mayor	menor	menos de	

Humberto tiene quince años. Rogelio tiene dieciséis años.

1. Humberto tiene ______________ dieciséis años pero ______________ catorce años.
2. Humberto es ______________ que Rogelio.
3. Rogelio es ______________ que Humberto.

Hay ocho personas en la familia de Humberto. Hay cinco personas en la familia de Rogelio.

4. La familia de Humberto es ______________ que la familia de Rogelio.
5. La familia de Rogelio es ______________ que la familia de Humberto.
6. Hay un ______________ número de personas en la familia de Humberto.
7. Hay un ______________ número de personas en la familia de Rogelio.
8. En la familia de Humberto, hay ______________ cinco personas.
9. En la familia de Rogelio, hay ______________ ocho personas.

Humberto compró cinco aguacates. Rogelio compró diez aguacates.

10. Humberto compró un ______________ número de aguacates que Rogelio.
11. Rogelio compró ______________ cinco aguacates.
12. Humberto compró un número ______________ de aguacates.

Nombre: ______________________________ Fecha: ______________

7 La comida en España

What food is eaten in Spain? Match each dish on the left with its appropriate description in English on the right.

_____ 1. tortilla española

_____ 2. cochinillo asado

_____ 3. pulpo y mariscos

_____ 4. butifarra

_____ 5. fabada

A. bean stew
B. octopus and shellfish
C. a kind of sausage
D. Spanish omelet
E. a roasted piglet

Nombre: ______________________ Fecha: ______________

8 Una conversación en el mercado

Create a dialog between the two friends in the illustration, who are shopping at a Spanish market. Have them talk about the things they will be buying at the market and why they will buy them there as opposed to online, in a supermarket, or in a specialty shop.

____

____

____

____

____

____

____

____

____

____

____

Nombre: ______________________________ Fecha: ______________

9 En el supermercado

Imagine you work at a supermarket. Arrange the following foods by writing the name of each item in the appropriate space.

Nombre: ______________________________ Fecha: ______________

10 Categorías

Choose the word in each row that does not belong in the group.

1. jamón	carne	arroz	chorizo
2. fresa	naranja	plátano	maíz
3. agua	queso	jugo	leche
4. huevos	guisantes	habichuelas	pimientos
5. uvas	manzanas	fresas	zanahorias
6. queso	leche	papa	mantequilla

11 La paella de Julián

Complete the following sentences with the preterite forms of the verbs in parentheses.

1. Julián ____________________ paella valenciana. (preparar)
2. Nosotros lo ____________________. (ayudar)
3. Yo ____________________ la receta en la internet. (buscar)
4. Hernán y Laura ____________________ los ingredientes en el mercado. (comprar)
5. Laura ____________________ el pollo y el pescado en aceite y ajo. (cocinar)
6. Hernán ____________________ las verduras antes de ponerlas en la paella. (lavar)
7. Cuando la paella ____________________ de cocinar, yo ____________________ la estufa. (terminar, apagar)
8. ¿Por qué tú no ____________________? (ayudar)

Nombre: ______________________________ Fecha: ______________

12 ¿Qué dieron?

Write complete sentences, saying what everyone gave to the food drive, based upon the drawing.

MODELO: Mariana

Mariana dio dos latas de guisantes.

1. yo ______________________________

2. Esteban ______________________________

3. Jorge y Carmen ______________________________

4. nosotros ______________________________

5. tú ______________________________

Nombre: ______________________________ Fecha: ______________

13 ¿Ya estuvieron allí?

You need to find out if the following people have already been to the main attractions in Madrid, Spain. Write questions, using a name or pronoun from the list, the preterite form of the verb *estar* and a place marked in the map. Follow the model.

MODELO: ¿Ya estuvo Pedro en la Plaza de Oriente?

Pedro	tú	Carlos	nosotros
Víctor y Nuria	Paloma	Uds.	Sofía

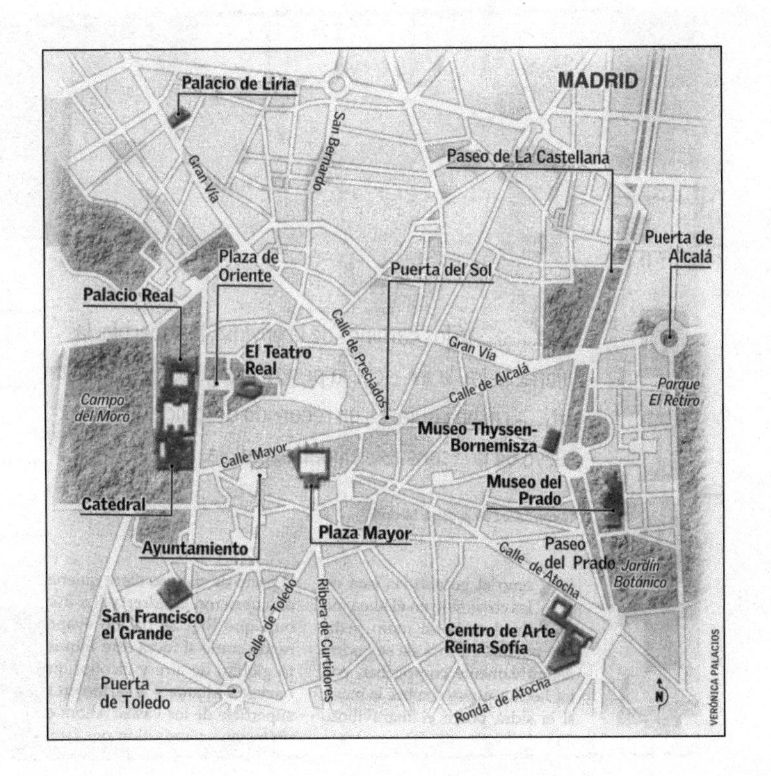

1. ______________________________
2. ______________________________
3. ______________________________
4. ______________________________
5. ______________________________
6. ______________________________
7. ______________________________

Nombre: ______________________ Fecha: ______________

Unidad 9

Lección A

1 Crucigrama

Complete the following crossword puzzle.

Horizontales

1. Las camisas son para hombres y las _____ son para mujeres.
3. Para dormir, necesito un _____.
6. Rojo y azul hacen _____.
8. El chocolate es de color _____.
9. Rojo y blanco hacen _____.

Verticales

2. La zanahoria es de color _____.
3. Pongo el _____ en el zapato.
4. Compro una corbata en el departamento de ropa para _____.
5. La señorita tiene zapatos de _____.

Nombre: ______________________ Fecha: ______________

2 Las partes del cuerpo

Look at the drawing and identify the parts of the body.

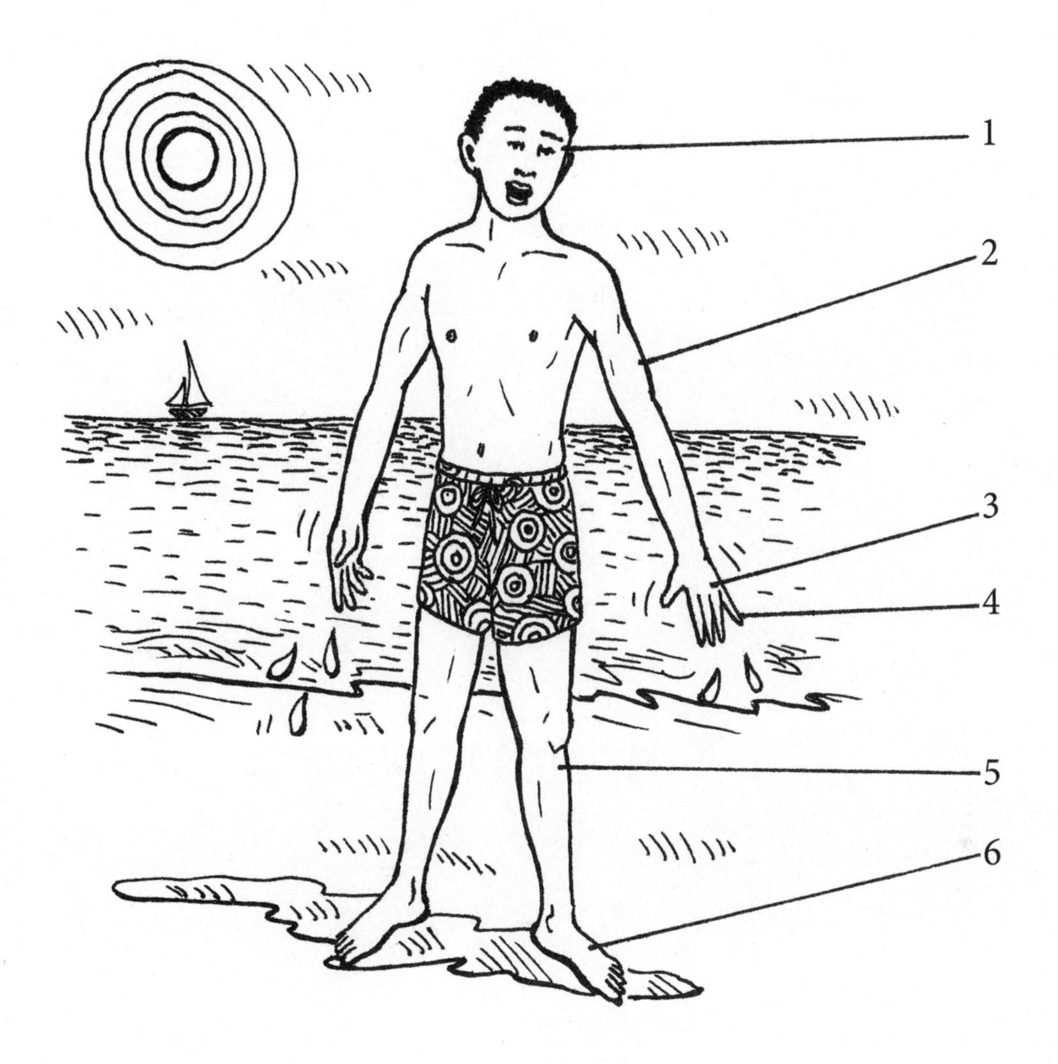

1. ______________________
2. ______________________
3. ______________________
4. ______________________
5. ______________________
6. ______________________

Nombre: ______________________________ Fecha: ______________

3 Categorías

Choose the word in each row that does not belong in the group.

1. camisa	traje	vestido	corbata
2. verde	algodón	morado	marrón
3. zapato bajo	bota	zapato de tacón	abrigo
4. blusa	mano	pierna	cabeza
5. medias	corbata	blusa	vestido
6. traje de baño	ropa interior	pijama	bota

Nombre: ______________________ Fecha: ____________

4 ¿Qué prefieres?

Complete the following survey about your preferences in clothes and colors. Answer each question, omitting the noun. Follow the model.

MODELO: ¿Prefieres las botas negras o las botas marrones?
Prefiero las negras/las marrones.

1. ¿Prefieres los pijamas blancos o los pijamas rojos?

   ____

2. ¿Prefieres las camisas rosadas o las camisas azules?

   ____

3. ¿Prefieres los trajes de baño rojos o los trajes de baño negros?

   ____

4. ¿Prefieres la ropa interior blanca o la ropa interior anaranjada?

   ____

5. ¿Prefieres las corbatas rojas o las corbatas amarillas?

   ____

6. ¿Prefieres los vestidos negros o los vestidos morados?

   ____

7. ¿Prefieres los trajes azules o los trajes grises?

   ____

8. ¿Prefieres las blusas verdes o las blusas marrones?

   ____

Nombre: ______________________ Fecha: ____________

5 En el departamento de ropa

Complete each sentence with the preterite tense of the verb in parentheses.

1. Álvaro ______________ dinero a sus padres. (pedir)
2. Los muchachos ______________ a la sección de zapatos. (correr)
3. Las muchachas ______________ al segundo piso. (subir)
4. Nosotros ______________ mucha ropa bonita. (ver)
5. Josefina ______________ una blusa rosada de seda. (escoger)
6. Yo ______________ la camisa blanca de algodón. (preferir)
7. El señor Quiroga ______________ muchas botas. (vender)
8. Tú ______________ con un traje de baño, ¿verdad? (salir)

6 Otra vez

Rewrite the following sentences, replacing the words in italics with the words in parentheses. Make any necessary changes.

MODELO: *Guillermo* durmió toda la tarde. (los muchachos)
Los muchachos durmieron toda la tarde.

1. *Mabel y yo* comimos en la cafetería. (tú)

____

2. *Yo* pedí la sopa de pescado. (Mabel)

____

3. Después, *nosotros* corrimos por el parque. (yo)

____

4. *Ella* prefirió montar en bicicleta. (Uds.)

____

5. *Mis padres* nos permitieron ir a España. (Mamá)

____

6. *Yo* aprendí a preparar paella. (nosotros)

____

Nombre: ______________________ Fecha: ______________

7 ¿Quién fue?

Imagine you work at a store and the boss has just returned from a trip. Answer her questions, using the cues in parentheses.

MODELO: ¿Quién me escribió la carta? (nosotros)
Nosotros la escribimos.

1. ¿Quién abrió la tienda? (Lorenzo)

 ____

2. ¿Quién encendió las luces? (Magdalena)

 ____

3. ¿Quién pidió más camisas azules? (yo)

 ____

4. ¿Quién salió de vacaciones? (Pablo)

 ____

5. ¿Quién prefirió trabajar los sábados? (Iván y Tere)

 ____

6. ¿Quién recogió la ropa? (nosotros)

 ____

Nombre: ______________________________ Fecha: ______________

8 Panamá.com

The following web page about Panama has some words missing. Complete it with the words from the list.

Atlántico un canal inversionistas Colón playas
tarifas el turismo balboas barcos

La República de Panamá

Panamá es un país comercial. Uno de sus servicios más importantes es (1) ____________, ya que tiene (2) ____________ de agua cálida y arena blanca. También tiene (3) ____________ que conecta los océanos Pacífico y (4) ____________. Por allí pasan más o menos 14.000 (5) ____________ en un año. La Zona Libre de (6) ____________ es muy atractiva para los (7) ____________, porque allí pueden hacer negocios sin (8) ____________ de importación y exportación. Las transacciones se hacen en dólares americanos y también en (9) ____________, la moneda de Panamá.

Nombre: ______________________ Fecha: ______________

9 El Canal de Panamá

Imagine you're writing an article for a travel guide about the Panama Canal. Use the following questions as a guide, and add any other information you think is appropriate.

- ¿Cuándo fue construido? ¿Quién lo construyó?
- ¿Por qué es importante?
- ¿Quiénes lo utilizan?
- ¿Cómo funciona?
- ¿Es necesario pagar?
- ¿Qué proyectos hay para el futuro?

Nombre: ______________________________ Fecha: ______________

10 Comprar por catálogo

The following people ordered clothes through a catalog. Write complete sentences, saying what everyone ordered.

MODELO: 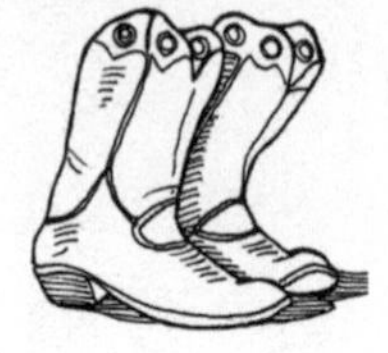 José
José pidió botas.

1. Olga

____

____

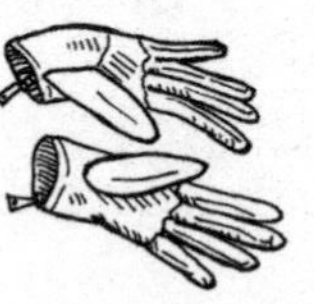

4. Rubén y Rodrigo

____

____

2. la Sra. Costas

____

____

5. tú

____

____

3. yo

____

____

6. el Sr. Márquez

____

____

Nombre: ______________________ Fecha: ____________

11 ¿Adónde fueron y qué hicieron allí?

Combine elements from each column to write seven complete sentences, saying where everyone went and what they did there. Follow the model.

MODELO: Germán fue a la biblioteca y sacó un libro.

Germán	la biblioteca	dar un paseo
nosotros	el cine	comprar ropa
yo	el parque	comer paella
Pamela	la piscina	sacar un libro
los muchachos	el mercado	mirar una película
tú	la tienda	bailar
Toño y David	la fiesta	comprar frutas
Sonia	el restaurante	nadar

1. ______________________
2. ______________________
3. ______________________
4. ______________________
5. ______________________
6. ______________________
7. ______________________

12 La mejor fiesta

Complete the following paragraph with the preterite tense of the verbs *ser* and *ir*.

La fiesta del Club de Español (1)______________ en la casa de la profesora Camacho. Más de cuarenta estudiantes (2)______________ a la fiesta. Yo (3)______________ la primera persona en llegar. Todos comieron y bailaron mucho. A la medionoche, nosotros (4)______________ a buscar más comida. ¡(5)______________ la mejor fiesta del año!

Nombre: ______________________________ Fecha: ______________

13 ¿Quieres ir?

Complete the following telephone conversation, using the words from the list.

algo alguien alguna nada nadie ni ninguna tampoco

EDGAR: Hola, Luisa. ¿Vas a hacer (1)______________ esta tarde o esta noche?

LUISA: No, no voy a hacer (2)______________ ni esta tarde (3)______________ esta noche. ¿Por qué?

EDGAR: ¿Quieres ir de compras? Es el cumpleaños de Marta.

LUISA: ¿Es el cumpleaños de Marta? (4)______________ me lo dijo.

EDGAR: A mí me lo dijo (5)______________ en la clase de español. ¿Quieres ir?

LUISA: Sí, pero no tengo (6)______________ idea de qué comprarle. ¿Tienes tú (7)______________ idea?

EDGAR: No, yo (8)______________ sé qué comprar.

14 Lo contrario

Rewrite the following sentences to make them negative. Follow the model.

MODELO: Busco a alguien. / No busco a nadie.

1. Tú siempre llevas guantes.

____

2. Alguien debe hacerlo.

____

3. Quiero comprar algo.

____

4. Pedro también lo pidió.

____

5. Fue o Ana o Rosa.

____

6. Algunos niños lo saben.

____

7. ¿Buscan alguna receta?

____

Nombre: ______________________________ Fecha: ______________

Lección B

1 Identifica

Look at the following drawing and identify the items that are labeled.

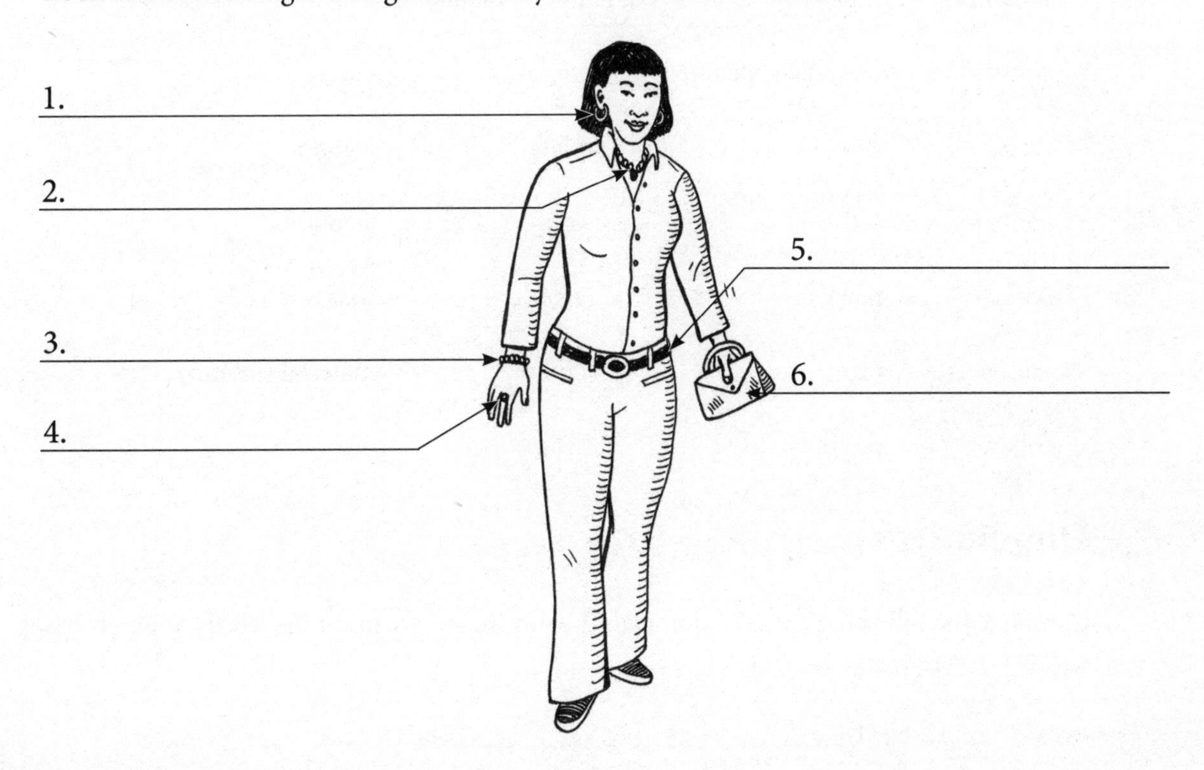

2 Completa

Complete the following sentences, using words from the list.

ascensor billetera cuero joyas larga paraguas perlas regalos

1. Lleva un ______________________ porque va a llover.
2. Recibí muchos ______________________ el día de mi cumpleaños.
3. Subo al décimo piso en un ______________________.
4. La bufanda no es corta; es ______________________.
5. Collares, pulseras y aretes son ______________________.
6. El cinturón de Arturo es de ______________________.
7. Tengo veinte dólares en mi ______________________.
8. Compramos un collar de ______________________.

Nombre: ______________________________ Fecha: ______________

3 Materiales

Of what materials can the following items be made? Choose the two most likely materials in each row.

MODELO: chaqueta: (cuero) (lana) plata

1. cinturón:	material sintético	perlas	cuero
2. arete:	oro	plata	algodón
3. pañuelo:	seda	oro	algodón
4. blusa:	plata	algodón	seda
5. bolso:	oro	cuero	material sintético
6. collar:	perlas	seda	oro

4 Diminutivos

Complete the following conversation with the diminutive forms of the words in parentheses.

PAPÁ: Hola, (1)______________________. (hija)

SILVIA: Hola. ¿Quieres un (2)______________________? (café)

PAPÁ: Sí, un (3)______________________. (poco)

SILVIA: Aquí tienes: café y un (4)______________________. (pan)

PAPÁ: Gracias, (5)______________________. (Silvia)

Nombre: ______________________ Fecha: ______________

5 Lo siento

Alicia wrote a letter of apology to Rodrigo. Complete it with the preterite forms of the verb *tener*.

Querido Rodrigo,

Siento mucho que mi familia y yo no fuimos a tu fiesta. Mis padres (1)______________ *que trabajar. Paola* (2)______________ *que estudiar para un examen y yo* (3)______________ *que ir al dentista. Luego esa noche, Paola y yo* (4)______________ *que cocinarle a mi abuelita. Sé que* (5)______________ *una buena fiesta, Rodrigo. Te prometo ir a la próxima.*

Tu amiga,

Alicia

Nombre: ______________________ Fecha: ____________

6 ¿Qué vieron?

Look at the following schedule for the TV station Telemadrid. Write complete sentences, using the preterite of the verb *ver* to say what the following people watched at the given times.

MODELO: Rubén / 14:00
Rubén vio Telenoticias.

1. Nora / 9:45

____

____

2. tú / 12:10

____

____

3. Hugo y Marco / 19:30

____

____

4. nosotros / 3:20

____

____

5. Gloria / 14:00

____

____

6. yo / 10:30

____

____

TELEMADRID

7.45 Documental: carreras asombrosas.
8.15 Los hombres de Harrelson.
9.00 Telenoticias sin fronteras.
9.45 En acción.
10.30 Cyberclub.
11.20 Shin Chan.
12.10 El príncipe de Bel-Air.
13.00 En pleno Madrid. Espacio de debate. «Presupuestos 2003: en qué se gastará nuestro dinero el Gobierno».
14.00 Telenoticias.
15.30 Cine de tarde. «Street Fighter: la última batalla». EE.UU. 1994. 108 min. Dir: Steven E. de Souza. Int: Raul Julia, Jean Claude Van Damme y Damian Chapa. Un hombre, Bison, quiere conquistar el mundo. Para ello, contrata a una serie de poderosos luchadores para que, por medio de la extorsión, llegar a lo que se propone.
17.35 Cine: una comedia. «Bitelchús». EE.UU. 1988. 92 min. Dir: Tim Burton. Int: Alec Baldwin, Geena Davis y Michael Keaton.
19.30 Fútbol es fútbol.
21.35 Cine: el megahit. «Dogma». EE.UU. 1999. 133 min. Dir: Kevin Smith. Int: Ben Affleck, Matt Damon y Linda Fiorentino. Dos ángeles caídos intentan retornar al cielo. Pero si logran su objetivo eliminarán a toda la raza humana.
0.10 Cine.es. «El día de la bestia». España. 1995. 103 min. Dir: Álex de la Iglesia. Int: Santiago Segura, Álex Angulo y Armando de Razza. Después de 25 años de estudiar el Apocalipsis de San Juan, el cura ángel Berriatua tiene la certeza de que el Anticristo nacerá el 25 de diciembre de 1995.
2.00 Cine: la noche de terror. «La Galaxia del terror». EE.UU. 1981. 78 min. Dir: B.D. Clark. Int: Ray Walston, Grace Zabriskie y Edward Albert, Jr.
3.20 Starsky y Hutch. «Los rehenes».
4.05 Pasados de vuelta.
4.30 Programación de laOtra.
6.30 Información Cultural CAM.

Nombre: ______________________________________ Fecha: ____________

7 ¿Qué hicieron?

What did Sergio's friends do to throw him a surprise birthday party? Write complete sentences, using the cues and the preterite forms of the verb *hacer*.

MODELO: Beatriz / una lista
Beatriz hizo una lista.

1. Manolo / una paella

____

2. yo / el postre

____

3. Carolina y Marta / un jugo

____

4. tú / una lista de juegos

____

5. Norma / los adornos

____

6. Luis / un dibujo cómico de Sergio

____

7. nosotros / muchas cosas

____

8. José y David / nada

____

Nombre: ______________________________ Fecha: ______________

8 ¿Qué sección dijeron que leyeron?

Summarize what section of the newspaper everyone said they read this morning. Look at the newspaper guide and choose a different section for each person. Use the preterite forms of the verbs *decir* and *leer*. Follow the model.

MODELO: Rocío
Rocío dijo que leyó la sección de deportes.

ÍNDICE

EDITORIALES	11	CULTURA/ESPEC	52
OPINIÓN	12	CARTELERA	60
CARTAS	14	ESQUELAS	63
NACIONAL	16	CLASIFICADOS	66
INTERNACIONAL	32	ECONOMÍA	67
AGENDA	43	DEPORTES	72
LOTERÍA	43	GENTE	80
SORTEOS	43	PASATIEMPOS	82
TIEMPO	44	HORÓSCOPO	82
SOCIEDAD	46	TV/RADIO	83

1. Rebeca y María

____

2. yo

____

3. Carlos

____

4. Uds.

____

5. Sarita

____

6. nosotros

____

7. tú

____

Nombre: ______________________________ Fecha: ______________

9 Correo electrónico

Complete Alejandra's e-mail with the preterite forms of the words from the list. One word is used more than once.

abrir	comprar	decir	empezar	ir
leer	oír	subir	ver	

De: Alejandra

Para: Vicente

Asunto:

Hola Vicente:

¿Quieres oír algo cómico? Ayer mi madre y yo (1)__________________ de compras. Ella (2)__________________ en el periódico y también (3)__________________ en la radio que iba a *(was going to)* llover y (4)__________________ que quería comprarme un paraguas nuevo. En la tienda, nosotros (5)__________________ al tercer piso, y allí, mi madre (6)__________________ el paraguas más grande del mundo. Ella lo (7)__________________. Al regresar a casa, (8)__________________ a llover. Yo (9)__________________ el paraguas pero hizo tanto viento que se lo llevó. Esta mañana, yo (10)__________________ decir que unos muchachos vieron un paraguas grande en el patio de su casa. ¿Qué te parece?

Hablamos más tarde,

Alejandra

Nombre: ______________________________ Fecha: ______________

10 Los productos de Ecuador

Choose the correct answer to complete the following statements about Ecuador.

1. Ecuador es uno de los principales... de flores en todo el mundo.

   A. importadores B. exportadores

2. Las temperaturas... de Ecuador favorecen los cultivos.

   A. estables B. inestables

3. Ecuador produce más o menos... de toneladas de plátanos al año.

   A. 8.000.000 B. 8.000

4. Los... forman parte de muchos platos típicos de Ecuador.

   A. cangrejos B. camarones

5. La exportación de... también es muy importante.

   A. autos B. petróleo

6. El sombrero tradicional de Ecuador se llama...

   A. sombrero ecuatoriano B. sombrero panamá

11 Ecuador y sus islas

Decide whether the following statements about Ecuador are *cierto* or *falso*. Write **C** or **F** in the space provided.

______ 1. Las islas Galápagos es uno de los destinos menos famosos de Ecuador.

______ 2. Las islas Galápagos se extienden por toda la línea ecuatorial.

______ 3. Las tortugas gigantes se encuentran en toda América del Sur.

______ 4. En las islas Galápagos hay muchas especies de peces.

______ 5. En 1990 sus aguas se convirtieron en un santuario para delfines.

______ 6. Los ecuatorianos hacen todo lo posible para proteger el ecosistema de las islas.

______ 7. Las islas Galápagos proporcionan importantes ingresos para la economía del país.

Nombre: ______________________ Fecha: ______________

12 Preguntas y respuestas

Match the questions on the left with the most appropriate response on the right. Write the letter of your choice in the space provided.

______ 1. ¿Dónde pago?	A. No, porque pagué con tarjeta de crédito.
______ 2. ¿Cómo va a pagar?	B. Para cambiar algo.
______ 3. ¿Para qué necesito el recibo?	C. En efectivo.
______ 4. ¿Te gusta el bolso?	D. Está en oferta. Cuesta veinte dólares.
______ 5. ¿Quién me puede ayudar?	E. Sí, es de buena calidad.
______ 6. ¿Cuánto cuesta el cinturón?	F. En la caja.
______ 7. ¿Te dieron cambio?	G. Está muy caro.
______ 8. ¿Por qué no lo compras?	H. El dependiente.

13 De compras

Unscramble the following dialog between a shopper and a clerk. Number the sentences in a logical order. The first one has been done for you.

______ ¿Cómo va a pagar?

__1__ Buenas tardes. Busco un regalo para mi madre.

______ ¿Qué tal este perfume?

______ Este bolso está en oferta especial. Sólo cuesta veinticinco dólares.

______ Aquí tiene cinco dólares de cambio y su recibo.

______ ¿Cuánto cuesta?

______ Está muy caro. ¿No tiene algo más barato?

______ Es bonito y de buena calidad. Bueno, lo compro.

______ Cuarenta dólares.

______ Muchas gracias.

______ En efectivo.

Nombre: ______________________ Fecha: ____________

14 ¿Con quién?

Belinda wants to know with whom everyone went shopping. Answer her questions affirmatively, using the appropriate pronouns.

MODELO: ¿Con quién fue Silvia? ¿Con Elena?
Sí, fue con ella.

1. ¿Con quién fue Lucas? ¿Con Nicolás?

   ____

2. ¿Con quién fueron tus hermanos? ¿Contigo?

   ____

3. ¿Con quién fue Sofía? ¿Con su madre?

   ____

4. ¿Con quién fue David? ¿Con Olga y Cristina?

   ____

5. ¿Con quién fueron Fernando y Anabel? ¿Conmigo?

   ____

6. ¿Con quién fuiste tú? ¿Con Miguel y Pedro?

   ____

7. ¿Con quién fue Mónica? ¿Con Anabel y conmigo?

   ____

8. ¿Con quién fueron tus amigos? ¿Con Miguel y contigo?

   ____

Nombre: ____ Fecha: ________________

Unidad 10

Lección A

1 Deportes y pasatiempos

Everyone did something fun this year. Look at the drawing and write what each person played or did. Follow the model.

MODELO:  Sebastián
Sebastián jugó al básquetbol.

1.  Armando

____

____

2.  nosotros

____

____

3.  Paula y Ana

____

____

4.  yo

____

____

5.  tú

____

____

6.  Gabriela

____

____

Nombre: ______________________________ Fecha: ______________

2 ¿Qué tienen que hacer?

Everyone is busy this afternoon. Look at the drawings and write what everyone has to do. Follow the model.

MODELO:  Clara
Clara tiene que ir al dentista.

1. yo

____

____

5.  Pepe

____

____

2. Jorge

____

____

6.  Liliana

____

____

3. Gloria

____

____

7.  Eva y Julio

____

____

4. nosotros

____

____

8.  tú

____

____

Nombre: ______________________________ Fecha: ______________

3 Sopa de letras

Find and circle seven school subjects in the word square below. The words may read horizontally, vertically or diagonally.

M	H	T	G	M	H	Ó	A	L	B	S
A	E	I	B	I	R	I	R	Y	I	U
T	R	S	S	N	X	P	T	J	O	Z
E	Q	U	P	T	C	K	E	Z	L	Ó
M	U	Í	T	A	O	W	O	Á	O	P
Á	L	P	H	F	Ñ	R	D	R	G	A
T	I	É	R	T	Y	O	I	I	Í	M
I	Z	X	C	V	B	N	L	A	A	A
C	O	M	P	U	T	A	C	I	Ó	N
A	R	Q	F	Í	S	X	Á	O	N	B
S	T	R	I	N	G	L	É	S	É	I

4 Comparando clases

Complete the following comparisons with the school subjects of your choice.

MODELO: Biología es la clase más divertida.

1. ______________________ es más interesante que ______________________.
2. ______________________ es más aburrida que ______________________.
3. ______________________ es menos fácil que ______________________.
4. ______________________ es tan difícil como ______________________.
5. ______________________ fue la mejor clase del año.
6. ______________________ fue la peor clase del año.

Nombre: ______________________ Fecha: ____________

5 ¿Qué hicieron el jueves?

Many people went out on Thursday. Answer the questions about what they did, based on the information found in the following entertainment guide.

23/01 jueves

MÚSICA

Inconsciente Colectivo en concierto acústico, este jueves, en el Jazz Café, San Pedro, 10 p. m.
Entrada: ¢1.500.
Teléfono: 253-8933.

ARTES

Séptimo Salón Nacional de Artes Nueva Acrópolis.
Pinturas, foto grafías y esculturas del grupo Nueva Acrópolis. Galería Nacional, Museo de los Niños. De *lunes* a *viernes*, de 9 a. m. a 4:30 p. m. *Sábados* y *domingos*, de 10 a. m. a 5 p. m.
Entrada: gratuita.
Teléfono: 258-4929.

CINE

Saving Grace (*El jardín de la Alegría*), película que forma parte del I Festival de Cine Británico que presentará la Sala Garbo, Paseo Colón. Funciones a las 3, 5, 7 y 9 p. m.
Entrada: ¢1.500.
Teléfono: 222-1034.

BOHEMIA

La Casa de la Urraca, Tibás, lo invita a disfrutar de la música cubana del grupo Chocolate, 10 p. m.
Entrada ¢1.500.
Teléfono: 385-5994.

1. Augustín escuchó un concierto acústico. ¿Adónde fue?

   ____

   ____

2. Nosotros fuimos a la Sala Garbo. ¿Qué vimos?

   ____

   ____

3. Mauricio y Cecilia fueron a La Casa de la Urraca. ¿Qué escucharon?

   ____

   ____

4. Yo vi arte del grupo Nueva Acrópolis. ¿Adónde fui?

   ____

   ____

5. Clara fue al concierto de Inconsciente Colectivo. ¿Cuánto costó?

   ____

   ____

6. ¿A qué hora empezó el concierto del grupo Chocolate?

   ____

   ____

Nombre: ______________________ Fecha: ____________

6 Todos aprendieron algo

What did everyone learn to do this past year? Combine elements from each column and use the preterite tense of the verb *aprender* to write ten complete sentences.

MODELO: Flor aprendió a preparar paella.

Flor	tocar	al ajedrez
yo	montar	la cumbia
Carlota	jugar	a caballo
Juan y Pablo	leer	por internet
tú	ahorrar	paella
mis primos	navegar	una motocicleta
nosotros	preparar	el piano
Gerardo	patinar	un aguacate maduro
Rita y Tere	arreglar	en español
Adolfo y yo	escoger	dinero
mi mejor amigo	bailar	sobre ruedas

1. ______________________

2. ______________________

3. ______________________

4. ______________________

5. ______________________

6. ______________________

7. ______________________

8. ______________________

9. ______________________

10. ______________________

Nombre: ______________________________ Fecha: ______________

7 Este año fue…

Think about this school year. Write one or two paragraphs about it. Describe the classes you took. Say some things you did with your friends. Mention one or two things you learned to do. Conclude by saying if it was a better or worse year than last year.

Nombre: ______________________________ Fecha: ______________

8 El Perú de los incas

Choose the correct completion for each statement about Peru.

1. El Imperio inca llegó a ser el imperio más grande…

   A. del mundo B. de los Andes

2. Los incas construyeron la ciudad de Machu Picchu…

   A. en una montaña B. junto a un lago

3. La capital del Imperio inca se llama…

   A. Machu Picchu B. Cuzco

4. *El quipu* es un sistema de…

   A. finanzas B. calles

5. El Imperio inca estaba (*was*) unido por un sistema de…

   A. túneles B. calles

6. Para cruzar precipicios los incas hicieron…

   A. túneles B. puentes

9 La cultura de Perú

You have read about Peru's history and culture. Match the Spanish word or phrase on the left with its meaning on the right. Write the correct letter in the space provided.

______ 1. Machu Picchu

______ 2. Cuzco

______ 3. Inti Raymi

______ 4. quechua

______ 5. papas a la huancaína

______ 6. mestizaje

A. la lengua de los incas

B. la combinación de las raíces indígena y europea

C. una ciudad de piedra arriba de una montaña

D. un plato que combina ingredientes indígenas y españoles

E. la capital del Imperio inca

F. un festival en honor del sol

Nombre: ______________________ Fecha: ______________

10 De viaje por Perú

Think about what you have read about Peru. Imagine that you traveled there on vacation and were impressed by the history of the Incas. Write a paragraph including information about the following aspects of their empire and culture and any other appropriate information you would like to include.

- their language
- their religion
- their cities and architecture
- their economy

Nombre: ______________________________ Fecha: ______________

Lección B

1 De viaje

The following people are looking for travel buddies. Read the ads and then decide if the statements that follow are *cierto* or *falso*. Write **C** or **F** in the space provided.

Compañeros de ruta

Argentina

■ Busco compañeros de ruta para realizar paseos en bicicleta por Buenos Aires. Nos reunimos los sábados, a las 17, en 11 de Septiembre y Echeverría, en Belgrano. Escribir a: *marceloalejandro32@hotmail.com*

■ Mi nombre es Pablo y estoy armando un viaje al norte argentino en moto. Busco compañera de ruta para compartir el viaje y la experiencia. Escribir a: ***pablopio20@hotmail.com***

■ Tengo 25 años, soy Federico y con un amigo estamos planeando un viaje de mochileros para el verano. El lugar elegido es Mendoza (Cañón del Atuel) y también Bariloche. Pensábamos sumar a alguien más. Escribir a: ***fricofontan@hotmail.com***

■ Mi nombre es Diego, soy rosarino y estoy armando un viaje por el Sur para el verano. Busco compañero de ruta de entre 18 y 25 años, tipo mochilero. Escribir a: ***diegoe25@hotmail.com***

■ Soy Pablo, tengo 24 años y busco compañeros de ruta para viajar a fines de este mes hacia los Valles Calchaquíes, en Salta. La idea es compartir una buena experiencia, hacerse amigos y ahorrar gastos. Escribir a: ***pabloiglesias1@hotmail.com***

Europa

■ Me llamo Daniel, tengo 56 años y busco compañía con buena onda para viajar a España, Portugal y Marruecos. Escribir a: **lbecontabilidad@arnet.com.ar**

■ Tengo 45 años y busco compañeros de ruta para viajar a al sur de España, para visitar Córdoba, Sevilla y Granada. Me llamo Alejandro. Escribir a: ***alejantulo@hotmail.com.ar***

_______ 1. Los paseos en bicicleta por Buenos Aires son los domingos.

_______ 2. Pablo va a ir al norte de Argentina en moto.

_______ 3. Federico y un amigo quieren ir a España.

_______ 4. Diego busca un compañero de ruta entre 18 y 25 años.

_______ 5. A Pablo le gustaría compartir una buena experiencia con nuevos amigos.

_______ 6. A Daniel le gustaría viajar al sur de Argentina.

_______ 7. Alejandro piensa viajar al sur de España.

Nombre: ______________________________ Fecha: ______________

2 Ahora tú

Now it is your turn to write an ad for a travel friend. Imagine you can travel to a Spanish-speaking country this summer. First, answer the following questions. Then, use the information in your answers and the outline below to write your ad.

1. ¿Adónde vas a viajar y cuándo?

____

2. ¿Qué medio de transporte piensas usar?

____

3. ¿Con quién te gustaría compartir esta experiencia?

____

Me llamo... Tengo ... años. Busco compañeros de ruta para viajar a... en... Vamos a salir el... y volver el... Me gustaría conocer personas que son... Escribir a...

____

____

____

____

____

____

____

____

____

Nombre: ______________________________ Fecha: ______________

3 Oportunidades

If you are bilingual in English and Spanish, you could work in a Spanish-speaking country. Here are some ads taken from newspapers in Latin America. Write the number of the ad next to the name of the profession in Spanish.

______ secretaria ______ profesor de inglés ______ agente de turismo

MULTINATIONAL COMPANY
Seeks
PRESIDENTIAL ASSISTANT

- Five-year experience in managerial or presidential secretary position in multinational companies.
- Bilingual Spanish-English
- Perfect knowledge of Windows & Office software
- Excellent planning an interpersonal skills as well as time management.

WE OFFER: Excellent compensation benefits according to law, professional development and good working environment.

If you fulfill the requirements, please send your C.V. with photo to EL TIEMPO post box No. 6739.

1.

C TO C
COAST TO COAST ADVENTURES

Travel Agent / Tour Operator
Reservations

- Bilingual written & spoken (Spanish / English)
- Use of e-mail and Microsoft programs
- Good public relations skills
- Able to work from **Monday to Friday half a day**
- Salary: ¢85.000 monthly
- Experience in this position (at least a year)

Send your resume via fax: 225-6055

2.

International Company
Requires
English Teacher or Academic Advisors

Ages between 20-45, great appeareance, experience living in a foreign country and able to work inmediatly.

Transversal 18 No. 101-21

3.

Think of two other professions that would require bilingual skills:

____

____

Nombre: ______________________ Fecha: ____________

4 ¿Qué profesión?

Read what the following people like to do. Then write what his or her profession should be. Follow the model.

MODELO: BETO: Me gustaría enseñar español.
TÚ: Pienso que debes ser maestro.

arquitecto	artista	banquera	cocinero	dentista
programadora	maestro	médica	veterinaria	

1. ARTURO: Me gustaría diseñar casas.

   TÚ: ______________________

2. MATILDE: Me gustaría programar computadoras.

   TÚ: ______________________

3. FERNANDO: Me gustaría dibujar y pintar.

   TÚ: ______________________

4. LORENA: Me gustaría trabajar con animales.

   TÚ: ______________________

5. YOLANDA: Me gustaría trabajar en una clínica.

   TÚ: ______________________

6. GERMÁN: Me gustaría cocinar para muchas personas.

   TÚ: ______________________

7. ROXANA: Me gustaría trabajar en un banco.

   TÚ: ______________________

8. ROBERTO: Me gustaría arreglar dientes.

   TÚ: ______________________

Nombre: ______________________ Fecha: ____________

5 Color y personalidad

Do you think colors define personality? Look at the following web page and answer the questions that follow.

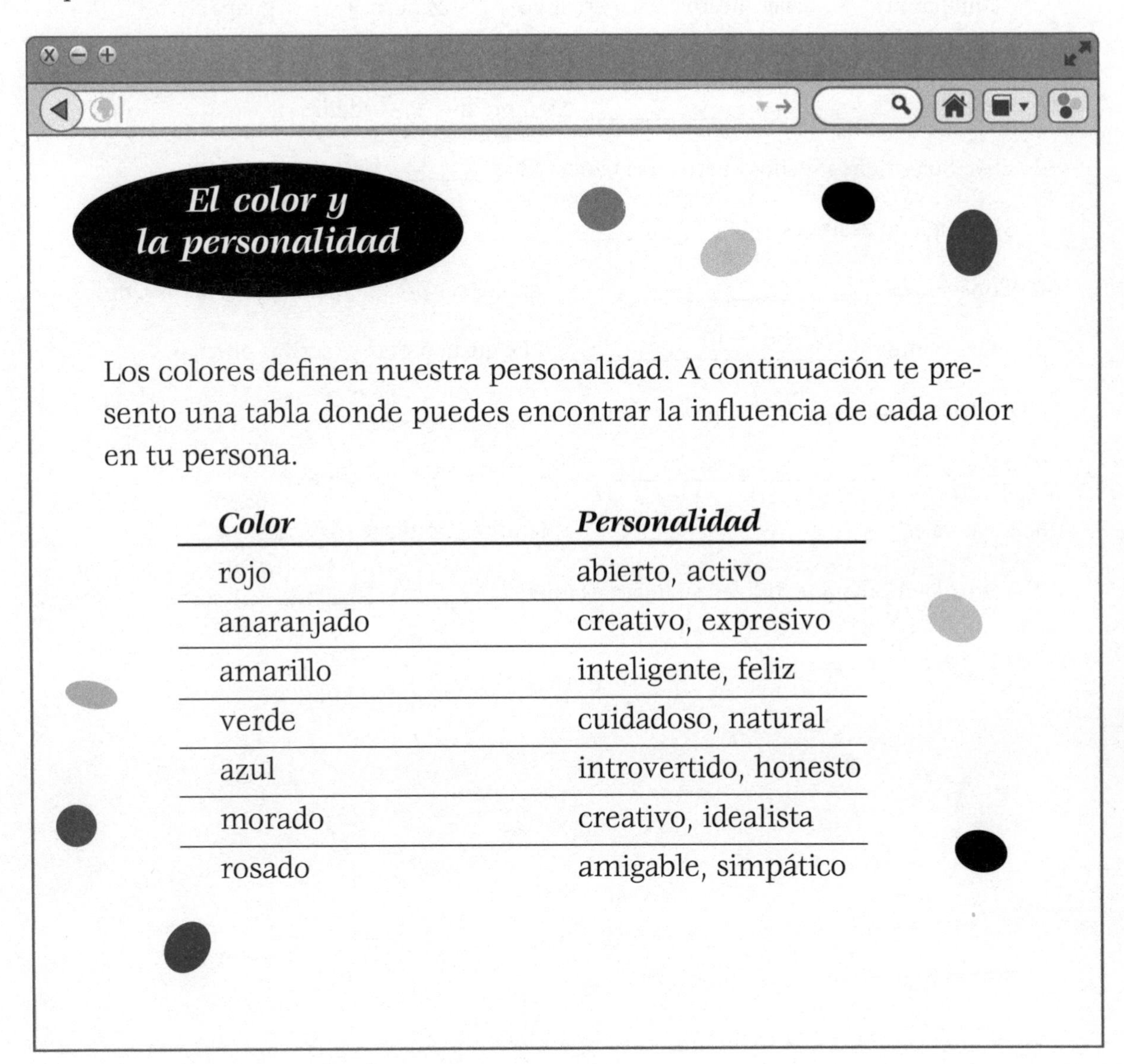

El color y la personalidad

Los colores definen nuestra personalidad. A continuación te presento una tabla donde puedes encontrar la influencia de cada color en tu persona.

Color	*Personalidad*
rojo	abierto, activo
anaranjado	creativo, expresivo
amarillo	inteligente, feliz
verde	cuidadoso, natural
azul	introvertido, honesto
morado	creativo, idealista
rosado	amigable, simpático

1. Escoge tu color favorito de la página web. ¿Cuál es?

____

2. ¿Qué dice la página web sobre cuál es tu personalidad?

____

3. ¿Es esa tu personalidad? Si no, ¿cómo eres?

____

Nombre: ______________________________ Fecha: ______________

6 ¿Cómo es?

Complete the following sentences, using words from the list.

ambiciosa	aventurero	creativo	generosa	guapa
honesto	organizado	popular	rico	

1. Franco es ________________________. Siempre dice la verdad.
2. El Sr. Soles tiene mucho dinero en el banco. Él es ________________________.
3. Mi amiga no es fea; es ________________________.
4. Consuelo es ________________________; quiere ser presidente de los Estados Unidos.
5. Javier es muy ________________________. Le gusta pintar y escribir poemas.
6. A Ernesto le gusta viajar mucho; es muy ________________________.
7. Amalia es ________________________. Ella tiene muchos amigos.
8. Eugenia es ________________________. Siempre comparte sus cosas.
9. Tomás siempre pone todo en su lugar; es muy ________________________.

Nombre: ______________________________ Fecha: ______________

7 Este verano

What are you doing this summer? Are you going to work? Are you going to travel? Write one or two paragraphs about your plans for this summer. Include what you have to do as well as things you would like to do.

____

____

____

____

____

____

____

____

____

____

____

____

____

____

Nombre: ______________________________ Fecha: ______________

8 Relato de un viaje al mundo de los mayas

Imagine you take a trip to Central America to know more about Mayan culture. Write a blog entry of your experience. You can use the following outline as a guide.

1. Start the blog on a certain date.
2. Mention what interests you about Mayan civilization.
3. Mention which Mayan ruins you tour and what you see there.
4. Mention which cities with Mayan population you visit.
5. Describe the current lifestyle of Mayas in those cities.
6. Mention what the Mayas want to know about your culture.
7. Describe how you feel about the overall experience.

____

____

____

____

____

____

____

____

____

____

____

____

____